THE MAGNIFICENT MARIO

MIKE LEONETTI   ILLUSTRATIONS BY **GARY CHATTERTON**

NORTH WINDS PRESS
Toronto New York London Auckland Sydney
Mexico City New Delhi Hong Kong Buenos Aires

Acknowledgements
Books written by these authors were consulted: Mike Bynum, Ron Cook, Chuck Finder, Lawrence Martin,
Dave Molinari, Paul Romanuk, Jean Somnor; Newspapers and Magazines: *The Globe and Mail*,
Pittsburgh Post-Gazette, *Sports Illustrated*, *The Hockey News*, *Toronto Star*;
Websites: hockeyreference.com, website of the QMJHL, Youtube.com, NHL.com, Hockeybuzz.com;
Videos: Minnesota North Star TV broadcasts of Game 2 and Game 6 of the 1991 Stanley Cup Finals;
Record Books: *NHL Guide and Record Book*, *Total Stanley Cup*.

The hockey events depicted in this book about the career and achievements of Mario Lemieux are all true.

Library and Archives Canada Cataloguing in Publication

Leonetti, Mike, 1958-
The magnificent Mario / Mike Leonetti ; illustrations by Gary Chatterton.

ISBN 978-1-4431-0705-1

1. Lemieux, Mario, 1965- --Juvenile fiction. I. Chatterton, Gary II. Title.

PS8573.E58734M34 2011   jC813'.54   C2011-902072-6

This story is dedicated to Mario Lemieux —
a true hockey legend.

— *M.L.*

There was just a minute left in the game, but it wasn't going fast enough for me. Finally, the buzzer sounded. The Maroons celebrated their 5–1 win over our team.

I skated out to our goalie, Claude, and patted him on his helmet. He always took losing hard.

"You played a good game," I said. "Don't worry. We're just in a slump. We'll get better."

In the car, I thought about all the games we'd lost.

"Dad," I said as we pulled into the driveway. "I don't think I want to play hockey anymore." I went to my room and plopped down on my bed.

A few minutes later, my dad came in and sat next to me.

"I know you're discouraged," he said. "But Max, think about Mario Lemieux." He handed me a hockey card. Lemeiux's rookie card!

"When he joined the Pittsburgh Penguins," he said, "they were the worst team in the league. But he keeps trying to make them winners. He's taken the Penguins from being at the bottom of the league to a Stanley Cup contender. They wouldn't be there if Mario had just given up.

"Work at getting better. You might see a big change." He got up to leave. "And remember: Mario played for the Hurricanes, just like you."

He was right. I couldn't just give up.

Lemieux had lived just one street over from our house in the west end of Montreal. Dad first saw him play when Mario was only four years old. Mario took the puck down the ice, went around two defensemen and then faked the goalie out of position to score a goal. Dad couldn't believe a kid could play like that.

I started to read everything I could about Mario. He was the best player in Canada when he played junior hockey for Laval. The Penguins selected him first overall in 1984, and he recorded 100 points as a rookie. Pittsburgh didn't have a good team, but Mario still recorded 100 or more points for six straight seasons. One year he scored 86 goals!

I told the guys all about him at practice. "We can be just like Mario," I said. "He hasn't given up and neither should we. Once, the Hurricanes were down by a score of 6–1. But Mario scored 6 goals, winning the game 7–6!"

"That's a great story, but Mario's not here," Claude said.

"Yeah, but if we work hard and help each other on the ice, maybe we can start winning more games."

I was a centre like Mario, and I wanted to play just like him. He scored picture-perfect goals, and was amazing with the puck. He even challenged Wayne Gretzky as the best player in the NHL. When someone asked him about not being on a championship team, he said, "I know I'll drink from that Cup one day. I just know it."

I really wanted to believe him, but it was hard. He was injured at the start of the 1990–91 season. Most of the guys on my team thought there was no way the Pens could win without him. But Pittsburgh had built a good team. They had Jaromir Jagr, Joe Mullen, Paul Coffey, Kevin Stevens, Mark Recchi, Bryan Trottier and goalie Tom Barrasso. Late in the year Mario finally returned. It was great to see big number 66 back in action!

"Now they have a chance to win," I said to my dad as we sat in the living room watching the Pens play the Canadiens one night. And then Mario scored the first goal of the game! A couple of days later, he scored twice as the Penguins knocked the New York Rangers out of first place in their division. Mario was getting stronger at just the right time.

As for the Hurricanes, we lost a few more games, but we were also winning more often. We all felt better about the team and were working hard to get into the playoffs.

One day Coach Fichaud pulled me aside.

"Max, you're playing a good game. And I'm impressed how you've inspired your teammates."

"We've been the worst for a while," I said, "but maybe we'll get better if we believe in ourselves and the team, like Mario has for the Penguins."

In April the Pens headed to the playoffs. They beat New Jersey in the first round and then Washington in the next. It was a bit scary in the third round when they lost the first two games to Boston, but they went on to win the next four! The Penguins were headed to the Stanley Cup finals!

When the Pens lost the first game against the Minnesota North Stars, I was really disappointed. But then Dad was assigned to shoot the next game in Pittsburgh. "Hey, Max, why don't you come with me? I know someone who can get us a ticket."

A chance to see Mario play in the Stanley Cup finals!

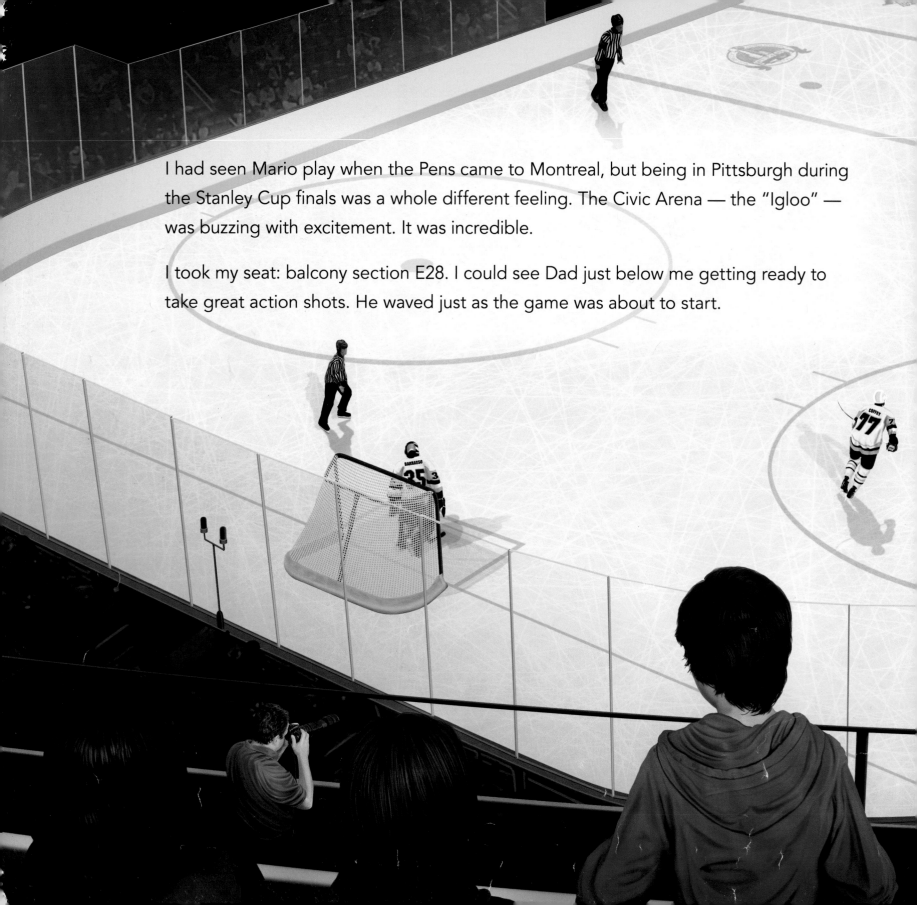

I had seen Mario play when the Pens came to Montreal, but being in Pittsburgh during the Stanley Cup finals was a whole different feeling. The Civic Arena — the "Igloo" — was buzzing with excitement. It was incredible.

I took my seat: balcony section E28. I could see Dad just below me getting ready to take great action shots. He waved just as the game was about to start.

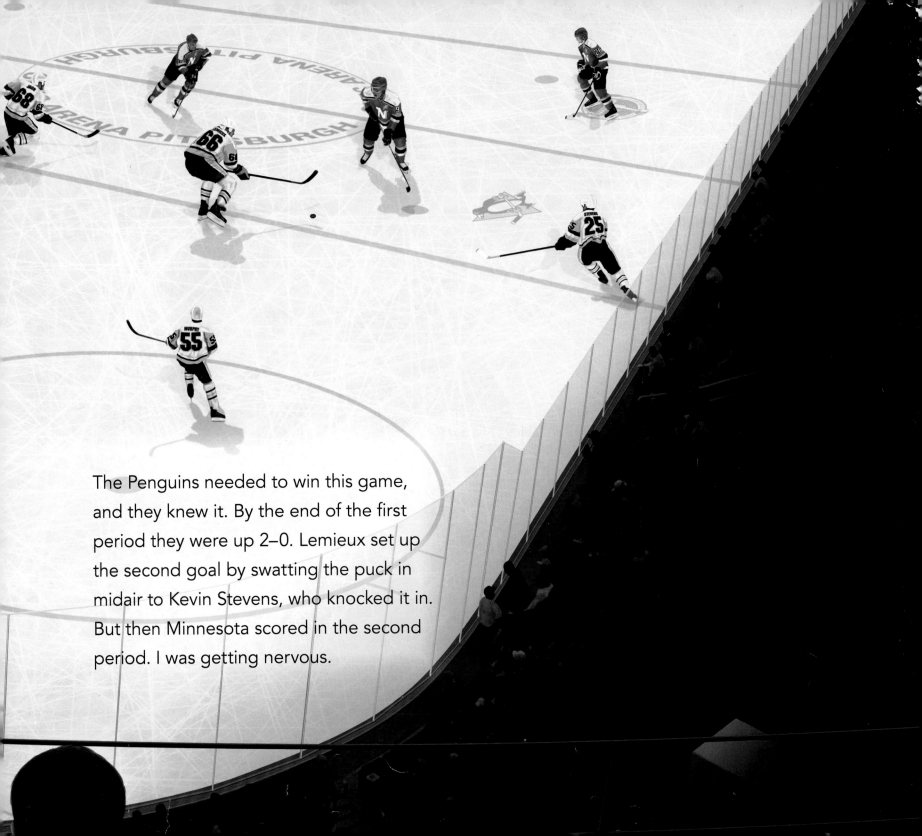

The Penguins needed to win this game, and they knew it. By the end of the first period they were up 2–0. Lemieux set up the second goal by swatting the puck in midair to Kevin Stevens, who knocked it in. But then Minnesota scored in the second period. I was getting nervous.

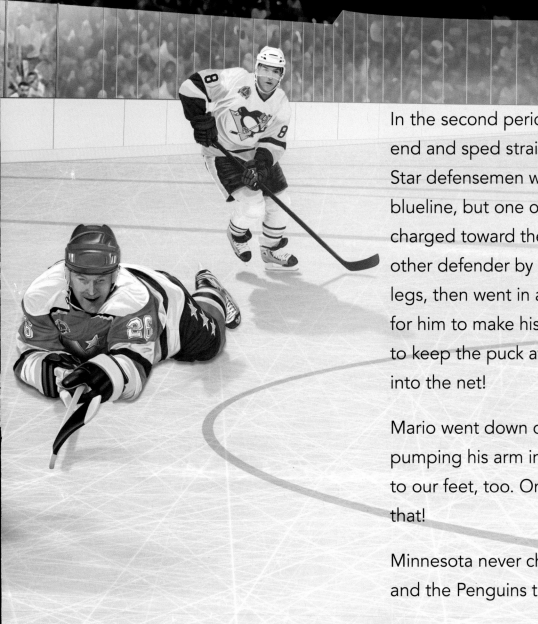

In the second period, Mario took the puck from his own end and sped straight up the ice. There were two North Star defensemen waiting for him at the Minnesota blueline, but one of them backed away a little as he charged toward the net. Mario got the puck past the other defender by putting it through the defender's legs, then went in all alone on the goalie and waited for him to make his move. Mario used his long reach to keep the puck away — and then backhanded a shot into the net!

Mario went down on the ice. But he was up in a flash, pumping his arm in the air. What a goal! We all jumped to our feet, too. Only the great Mario could score like that!

Minnesota never challenged Mario's magnificent goal, and the Penguins tied the series with a 4–1 victory.

21

On the plane ride home, all Dad and I talked about was Mario.

"I remember New Year's Eve, 1988," he said. "That night Mario scored five goals in five different ways: at even strength, short-handed, on a power play, on a penalty shot and then into an empty net. Nobody has ever done that. Pittsburgh won the game 8–6, and Mario was in on every goal," Dad said.

"I've seen some great players," he continued. "But I think Mario may be the best."

"I just hope he wins the Stanley Cup," I said. "Until then, he won't be thought of as a truly great player."

Back home, my skating, passing and shooting skills improved. My teammates seemed to get better, too. In practice, we stressed team play. The Hurricanes kept playing hard no matter what the score was, and we won more games. We even got the last playoff spot! In our game against the Maroons, we were down 4–2 heading into the third period, but we kept coming at them. We scored two goals, and I scored in the last minute to win 5–4 and knock them out of the playoffs. We celebrated like we'd won a championship!

In the second round, we were eliminated. It was disappointing, but after such a bad start to the season, we knew we'd gotten a lot better.

Mario missed his next game with an injury, and the Penguins lost. After he came back, Pittsburgh took a 3–2 lead in the series. The sixth game was in Minnesota, and again Dad was assigned to shoot the game. This time I stayed home and watched it on TV.

The Penguins opened the scoring just two minutes in when Joe Mullen scored. Then Mario took a long pass and galloped past the North Star defense to score another one of his amazing goals to make it 2–0. Mario set up three more goals with great passes. The Penguins won 8–0! Mario had finally won the Cup — just like he said he would!

Mario also won the Conn Smythe Trophy as the best player in the playoffs, but it was the Stanley Cup he really wanted. He towered over it as it was set on a table at centre ice. Finally he raised the Cup over his head and was mobbed by his teammates.

When Dad came home, he gave me a photograph he had taken of Mario. When Mario brought the Cup to the neighbourhood for a day, he signed my picture.

I put the photo on my dresser. Seeing it every day reminded me that winning is possible if you stick to it. I imagined holding a championship trophy of my own. We had almost done it this season. Maybe next season we could raise our own trophy just like Mario and the Penguins.

About Mario Lemieux

Mario Lemieux was born in Montreal on October 5, 1965, and played minor hockey in Ville Emard, where he grew up. He played junior hockey for the Laval Voisins of the Quebec Major Junior Hockey League, recording 282 points (133 goals, 149 assists) in 70 games during the 1983–84 season. He was selected first overall by the Pittsburgh Penguins in the 1984 NHL Entry Draft, and the 6'4", 230-pound Lemieux had the hopes of a troubled franchise placed on his broad shoulders. Although he was shy and spoke little English at the time, he let his talent do all the talking on the ice. He scored a goal on his first shift in his first NHL game on October 11, 1984, against the Boston Bruins. He finished his first year with 100 points and won the Calder Trophy as the best rookie in the league. The Penguins made the playoffs only once in his first six years, but then won the Stanley Cup in 1991 and 1992, with Mario taking the Conn Smythe Trophy both times. During the 1992–93 season, Mario was diagnosed with

Hodgkin's lymphoma, a form of cancer. After receiving radiation treatments, Lemieux returned to play and finished the year as the NHL's leading scorer with 160 points in just 60 games played. He would lead the league in points six times and be named the most valuable player on three occasions. The nine time all-star (six times on the first team) was also a part of Team Canada when they won the Canada Cup (1987), the gold medal at the Olympics (2002) and the World Cup (2004). He initially announced his retirement from the NHL after the 1996–97 season and was elected to the Hall of Fame in 1997. He decided to come back in the 2000–01 season and retired for good after the 2005–06 campaign. Lemieux finished with 690 goals and 1,033 assists for a total of 1,723 points in 915 games played. He scored 50 or more goals on six occasions and recorded 100 or more points ten times during his illustrious career. After his retirement Lemieux became a part owner of the Pittsburgh club and in 2009, the Penguins won the Stanley Cup for the third time in their history.

PRACTICAL GOURMET™
Inviting Asian Flavours

Pictured on front cover:
Pho Bo (Beef Noodle Soup),
page 194

Practical Gourmet
Copyright © Company's Coming Publishing Limited

All rights reserved worldwide. No part of this book may be reproduced, stored in a retrieval system or transmitted in any form by any means without written permission in advance from the publisher.

In the case of photocopying or other reprographic copying, a license may be purchased from the Canadian Copyright Licensing Agency (Access Copyright). Visit www.accesscopyright.ca or call toll free, 1-800-893-5777.

In the United States, please contact the Copyright Clearance Centre at www.copyright.com or call 978-646-8600.

Brief portions of this book may be reproduced for review purposes, provided credit is given to the source. Reviewers are invited to contact the publisher for additional information.

First Printing October 2009

Library and Archives Canada Cataloguing in Publication
Inviting Asian flavours. (Practical gourmet)
Includes index.
At head of title: Company's Coming.
ISBN 978-1-897477-05-2
1. Cookery, Asian. I. Series.
TX724.5.A1I58 2009   641.595   C2009-900638-3

Published by
Company's Coming Publishing Limited
2311 – 96 Street
Edmonton, Alberta, Canada T6N 1G3
Tel: 780-450-6223   Fax: 780-450-1857
www.companyscoming.com

Company's Coming is a registered trademark owned by
Company's Coming Publishing Limited

Printed in China

We acknowledge the financial support of the Government of Canada through the Book Publishing Industry Development Program (BPIDP) for our publishing activities.

Nutrition Information Guidelines

Each recipe has been analyzed using the Canadian Nutrient File from Health Canada, which is based upon the United States Department of Agriculture (USDA) Nutrient Database.
- If more than one ingredient is listed, such as butter (or hard margarine), or if a range is given (1 - 2 tsp., 5 - 10 mL), only the first ingredient or first amount is analyzed.
- The lesser number of servings is used if a range is stated.
- Ingredients indicating "sprinkle," "optional" or "for garnish" are not included in the nutrition information.
- Milk used is 1% M.F. (milk fat), unless otherwise noted.

Vera Mazurak, Ph.D (Nutritionist)

Acknowledgements

Inviting Asian Flavours *was created through the dedicated efforts of the people listed below:*

Editor-in-Chief	Eleana Yun
Research and Development Manager	Jill Corbett
Editorial Director	Tabea Berg
Editor	Sandra Bit
Recipe Editor	Michael Macklon
Senior Food Editor	Lynda Elsenheimer
Food Editor	Mary Anne Korn
Recipe Development Assistant	Stephanie Moore
Researcher	Frieda Lovig
Senior Recipe Tester	James Bullock
Recipe Testers	Allison Dosman
	Audrey Smetaniuk
Nutritionist	Vera Mazurak, Ph.D

Copy Editor/Proofreader	Laurie Penner
Editorial Assistant	Brett Bailey

Contributors	Patricia Meili-Bullock
	Jennifer Sayers-Bajger
	Laurie Stempfle

Creative Director	Heather Markham
Design and Production	Titania Lam
Photographer	Stephe Tate Photo
Photography Coordinator/ Image Editor	Heather Latimer
Food Stylist	Ashley Billey
Prop Stylists	Snez Ferenac
	Tiffany Day
Prep Assistant	Linda Dobos
Production Manager	Matt Bromley

Founding Author	Jean Paré
President	Grant Lovig
Vice President, Production and Creative	Alanna Wilson

Our special thanks to the following businesses for providing numerous props for photography:
Bowring
Shangrila La Exotic Home Decor
Stokes

We gratefully acknowledge the following suppliers for their generous support of our Test and Photography kitchens:
Broil King Barbecues   Lagostina®
Corelle®   Proctor Silex® Canada
Hamilton Beach® Canada   Tupperware®

Stock images:
dreamstime.com (divider pages)
fotolia.com (map on back cover)
gettyimages.com (map on page 8 and 9)

Contents

Lebanese 114

Malaysian 138

Thai 162

Vietnamese 188

The Company's Coming Legacy

Jean Paré grew up with an understanding that family, friends and home cooking are the key ingredients for a good life. A busy mother of four, Jean developed a knack for creating quick and easy recipes using everyday ingredients. For 18 years, she operated a successful catering business from her home kitchen in the small prairie town of Vermilion, Alberta, Canada. During that time, she earned a reputation for great food, courteous service and reasonable prices. Steadily increasing demand for her recipes led to the founding of Company's Coming Publishing Limited in 1981.

The first Company's Coming cookbook, *150 Delicious Squares*, was an immediate bestseller. As more titles were introduced, the company quickly earned the distinction of publishing Canada's most popular cookbooks. Company's Coming continues to gain new supporters in Canada, the United States and throughout the world by adhering to Jean's Golden Rule of Cooking: *Never share a recipe you wouldn't use yourself.* It's an approach that has worked—millions of times over!

A familiar and trusted name in the kitchen, Company's Coming has extended its reach throughout the home with other types of books and products for everyday living.

Though humble about her achievements, Jean Paré is one of North America's most loved and recognized authors. The recipient of many awards, Jean was appointed Member of the Order of Canada, her country's highest lifetime achievement honour.

Today, Jean Paré's influence as founding author, mentor and moral compass is evident in all aspects of the company she founded. Every recipe created and every product produced upholds the family values and work ethic she instilled. Readers the world over will continue to be encouraged and inspired by her legacy for generations to come.

Foreword

Good company and great food create a powerful combination. When laughter and conversation mix with the heady fragrance and flavours of delicious fare, we are not just sharing a meal—we are nourishing our lives. Artfully prepared dishes awaken the senses and please the palate. And here's the secret: It can all be so simple!

The Practical Gourmet series is designed to help home cooks create no-fuss, sumptuous food. *Inviting Asian Flavours* features full-colour photographs of each recipe, preparation tips and tricks, how-to photos, imaginative presentation ideas and helpful information on entertaining, so you and your guests can really savour the food—and your time together.

Asian cuisine is resplendent with exciting ingredients, gorgeous presentations and fabulous flavours—so it's no wonder that cooking Asian dishes at home is more popular in the west than ever. *Inviting Asian Flavours* takes you on a grand tour of Asia, offering a taste of what this broad and diverse region has to offer. The chapters explore the freshest flavours of Chinese, Indian, Japanese, Korean, Lebanese, Malaysian, Thai and Vietnamese cuisine. In a region made up of several billion people, the variety of food cultures is difficult to capture. Still, combining basic elements to create balanced tastes and contrasting textures seems to be a uniting quality of Asian cuisine.

Rediscover your favourite traditional dishes, or experiment with fusion dishes that express regional ingredients and cooking methods in a novel way. While Asian cooking can be perceived as daunting, these recipes were specifically designed to capture the flavours and character of Asian cuisine using a practical approach. Ingredients are readily available at your local grocery store or Asian supermarket and the methods are simple and straightforward. You can enjoy the time you spend in the kitchen, but truly savour the moments you spend around the table with your guests.

Vibrant Asian fare is perfect for entertaining. Dishes look impressive, taste exquisite and fill your home with wonderfully exotic fragrances—and yet, are perfect for creating memorable gatherings.

Intimate, exciting gatherings begin with the sophisticated but accessible recipes of *Inviting Asian Flavours*. Revel in the possibilities within these pages—it's never been

Lebanon

Snow-frosted summits. Industrious Mediterranean ports hailing ships. The legendary Cedars of God. Lebanon possesses an ancient culture forged by multiple influences—a rich, fascinating history that ultimately creates a uniquely blended food culture.

India

Women wrapped with vibrant saris. Curving marble domes adorning magnificent temples. Languid cows plodding along dusty roads. India's location along early spice routes endowed it with a rainbow of aromatic spices, shaping blends that are distinctive even between individual families.

Thailand

Brilliant green cliffs cascading to pristine beaches. Ornate shrines adorned with sun-drenched blossoms. A lone longboat gliding across a turquoise bay. Thailand's colourful culture embodies the elemental flavour combination of its cuisine: hot, sour, salty, sweet.

Malaysia

Lush rainforest cloaking vast limestone caverns. Soaring glass skyscrapers. Tiny sea turtles edging towards ocean surf. Malaysia's dynamic fusion melds indigenous culture, urbanized cities and neighbouring Asian influences—no surprise that the cuisine mirrors this diversity as well.

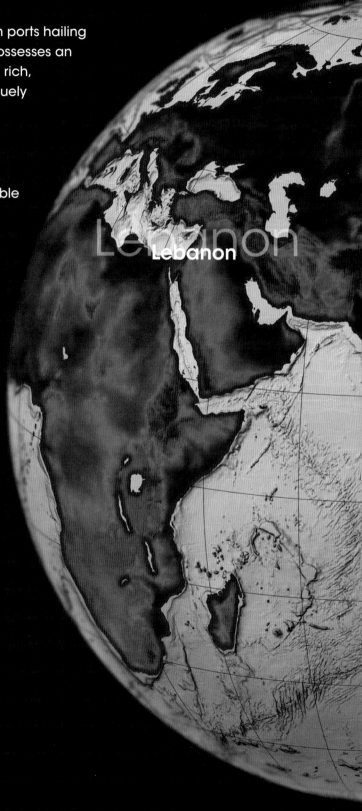

Lebanon

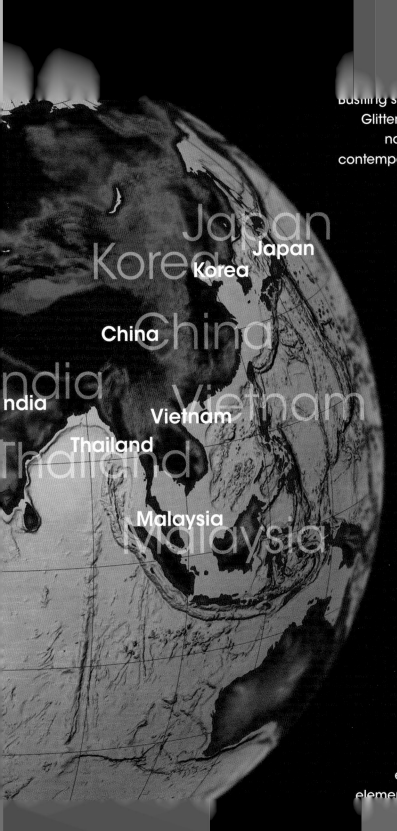

bustling seaside fish markets. Whispering teahouses.
Glittering, ultra-modern cities. Japan is an island
nation that balances illustrious tradition with
contemporary chic. The cuisine naturally follows suit
with simple, timeless dishes and
minimalist presentation.

Korea

Mountains draped in emerald foliage.
Narrow city streets pulsing with life.
Mineral-rich mudflats stretching along the
Yellow Sea. Korea translates as "Land of
the Morning Calm"—an intriguing
contrast to its culinary fare, which is often
spiced with lively chilies and kimchee.

China

Indomitable palaces enduring from
dynasties past. Booming metropolitan
centres rising skywards. Villagers
bearing yoked water buckets. China is
vast and ancient, and the most
populous country on Earth, its six
millennia of food culture founded on
making the most of what's at hand.

Vietnam

Bicycles laden with bushels of greens. Dark
vessels drifting from hazy harbours. Rice
fields thriving in flood plains. Vietnam's
climate varies radically, shaping an
extraordinarily diverse cuisine. But universal
elements do exist—fresh herbs with virtually every

Taking Tea

Tea is the most popular drink in Asian countries and is second only to water as the world's most consumed beverage. The teas featured here are commonly drunk at meals, specially made for guests or celebrated in ceremonies. The life-enhancing role of tea in these countries is a common thread they all share, despite their distinct cultural differences. Why not expand your culinary adventure into Asian cuisines and sample these delicious teas at your next gathering?

A short history of tea

Described by the classical Chinese philosopher Laozi (or Lao-tzu) as "the froth of the liquid jade," tea has been cultivated and consumed in Asia for centuries. *Camellia sinensis* plants grew wild in China until they were cultivated into tea gardens 5000 years ago.

The origins of tea drinking are shrouded in myth and lore. One legend tells that the Chinese Emperor Shen Nung (2737–2697 BC) discovered tea accidentally when three leaves from a tea bush fell into a bowl of boiled water he was drinking. Over the next several centuries, the Chinese aristocracy and upper classes developed a refined tea-drinking culture, complete with beautiful ceramic and porcelain teaware. Tea was also considered medicinal, and was taken as a tonic to enhance and maintain good health.

Tea seeds and bushes arrived in Japan by the 9th century AD and were planted near Kyoto. *Chanoyu* or "the way of tea" emerged in 16th century Japan and redefined tea drinking as an artistic ritual incoporating such Zen principles as harmony, respect and beauty. Participating in the ceremony put one on a higher spiritual plane. Also around this time, the Chinese perfected the production of sturdy, transportable black tea, allowing tea to travel to Europe, where it became a hit in many countries by the 18th century.

Types of tea

China: Jasmine flower tea
Jasmine flower tea is made by gently scenting white, green or pouching tea leaves with fresh jasmine flowers as the tea leaves dry and the flower petals open. Wonderfully scented and subtle and light in flavour and colour, it has been a favourite scented tea in China since the Song Dynasty (AD 960–1279). Fujian and Jiangsu Provinces along the east coast of China are known for their jasmine teas.

Japan: Genmaicha (gen-my-cha)
Genmaicha, or brown rice tea, is made by adding toasted rice kernels to Sencha or Bancha tea leaves (two popular green teas in Japan). The result is a refreshing green tea whose nutty flavour pairs well with Japanese food; for this reason, it is often served in Japanese restaurants. It is sometimes called "popcorn tea" because some rice kernels pop during the roasting process.

India: Masala chai
In India, *masala* chai is usually black tea (chai) brewed with a blend of spices (*masala*), whole milk and honey, sugar or syrup. Chai is sold by outdoor tea vendors, or chai *wallahs*, and is traditionally consumed from disposable, unglazed clay cups. The *masala* blend consists of at least four spices from an assortment that includes star anise, allspice, cardamom, cinnamon, cloves, coriander, fennel, ginger and peppercorns.

Korea: Chrysanthemum tea
Chrysanthemums are highly regarded in Korea, and symbolize honesty, purity and integrity. They are even celebrated with festivals during the autumn months. Beverages made from their flowers include chrysanthemum tea—an infusion made from the dried flowerheads steeped in hot water. The flowers are sometimes mixed with green tea for a different flavour. The tea has a clear to pale yellow colour and a light floral aroma and is sometimes used instead of green tea in the Korean tea ceremony, or *darye*.

Vietnam: Lotus tea

Vietnamese lotus tea is delicate, unique and rare, and is traditionally consumed at special events or festivals such as Tet, the Vietnamese New Year. Artisan tea scenters still use traditional, labour-intensive methods to create the tea, either stuffing intact lotus blossoms full of dried green tea leaves and letting them "steep" in the floral scent overnight, or applying the lotus flower stamens and pollen to dried tea leaves and baking them together in small batches over a period of several weeks.

Thailand: Lemon grass tea

Lemon grass is used extensively in Thai cuisine, so it's not surprising that this herb is also used to brew a lightly spicy, lemony and refreshing tisane. Lemon grass tea is drunk for its smooth, bright, clean flavour and its reputed medicinal qualities, which include aiding digestion, boosting energy and reducing fevers. It can be made either from dried leaves or from fresh lemon grass stalks that have been cut up, toasted until light brown and then steeped in hot water for several minutes.

Lebanon: Karkade (CAR-ca-day)

Karkade is the Arabic name for hibiscus tea, an infusion made from the dried calyces (outer leaves) of *Hibiscus sabdariffa* flowers. This ruby red and pleasingly tart tea is drunk hot or iced throughout the Middle East; Egyptians consider it to have been the preferred drink of the pharoahs, and in some Arab countries it is the custom to toast newlyweds with glasses of hibiscus tea. Karkade is also nutritious, as it is high in Vitamin C and antioxidants.

Malaysia: Black tea

At outdoor stalls across Malaysia, black tea is transformed into *teh tarik*, or pulled tea, a sweet concoction of hot tea and condensed milk that is poured quickly and repeatedly between two vessels from a height until a thick, frothy top forms. The "pulling" of *teh tarik* can be quite a spectacle, with brewers gathering for competitions and performances to show off their skills and how far above their heads they can drag a stream of tea.

Brewing the perfect cup of tea

Use fresh, cold, good-tasting water, filtered if possible. Make sure your kettle and teapot are clean, and preheat your pot or cup with warm water. When heating water for brewing, a good rule of thumb is that the darker the tea leaf, the hotter the water required to get the best results. White, green and herbal teas should be steeped at 160° to 175° F (71° to 79° C), oolong teas at 180° to 190° F (82° to 88° C) and black teas at 212° F (100° C). At 160° F (71° C), water is barely simmering; at 190° F (88° C), bubbles break the surface and steam rises; at 212° F (100° C), water is at a rolling boil. It may help to use a candy thermometer to check the water temperature the first time you steep a new tea.

Use loose tea if possible; bagged tea is considered inferior in quality and taste. Measure about 1 teaspoon (5 mL) of leaves per cup, either directly into your pot or cup, or into a teaball or infuser. Steep for 1 to 3 minutes for white, green and herbal teas and 3 to 5 minutes for black teas. Taste the tea for flavour before removing the leaves, and don't oversteep or your tea will become bitter. If using tea bags, follow the package directions. Serve tea immediately, either plain (preferable for white, green, herbal or oolong teas) or with milk, sugar, lemon, honey or even a dollop of raspberry jam.

Chinese cuisine aspires
to balance yin and yang by
playing colours, tastes and
textures off one another. Sweet
and sour, crisp and soft—infinite
combinations arise when pairing
one element with the next.
Allow guests to savour the
inherent contrasts in every bite.
For a dim sum twist, offer an array
of delicate morsels hot from a
bamboo steamer. Rouse the yin
and yang energy—arrange dark,
plush cushions for guests to sink
into, and string up vibrant
paper lanterns.

Chinese

Yin and Yang

Shrimp and Scallop Siu Mai

Sesame oil	1 tbsp.	15 mL
Finely chopped suey choy (green part only)	1 cup	250 mL
Finely chopped fresh shiitake mushrooms	1/2 cup	125 mL
Water chestnuts, finely diced	1/4 cup	60 mL
Chopped fresh chives	1 tbsp.	15 mL
Finely grated ginger root	1 tsp.	5 mL
Egg white (large), fork-beaten	1	1
Small bay scallops, chopped	6 oz.	170 g
Uncooked shrimp (peeled and deveined), chopped	6 oz.	170 g
Baby peas	2 tbsp.	30 mL
Finely diced orange pepper	2 tbsp.	30 mL
Soy sauce	2 tsp.	10 mL
Cornstarch	1 tsp.	5 mL
Round dumpling wrappers (see Tip, below)	30	30

Heat sesame oil in a large frying pan on medium. Add next 5 ingredients and cook for 3 minutes until cabbage is wilted and moisture is evaporated. Cool slightly.

Add next 7 ingredients and stir.

Spoon about 1 tbsp. (15 mL) filling onto centre of a wrapper (see How To, page 212). Moisten edges and gather up to form a cup shape. Repeat steps. Arrange dumplings in greased round cake pans. Steam over boiling water for 10 minutes until firm. Makes about 30 dumplings.

1 dumpling: 19 Calories; 0.6 g Total Fat (trace Mono, 0.1 g Poly, 0.1 g Sat); 10 mg Cholesterol; 1 g Carbohydrate; trace Fibre; 2 g Protein; 53 mg Sodium

ABOUT ROUND DUMPLING WRAPPERS
These can be found in Asian markets and in many large supermarkets. If you can't find round dumpling wrappers, use the square ones—as is, or cut into rounds.

ABOUT SIU MAI (SHOO-my)
Traditionally, this dumpling—with its characteristic basket or cup shape with exposed filling—is cooked in bamboo steamers that have been oiled on the bottom to keep the dumpling wrappers from sticking.

MAKE AHEAD
Cool cooked Siu Mai completely and refrigerate, covered, for up to one day. When ready to serve, re-steam over boiling water for five minutes.

GARNISH
chives
thinly sliced orange pepper

Pretty baskets that beckon. The lively hues of sweet peas and orange pepper peek through. Tender, mildly spiced shrimp and scallops round out this dim sum-style dumpling.

Shrimp Noodle Cakes
With Ginger Plum Sauce

Plum jam	1/2 cup	125 mL
Rice vinegar	1/3 cup	75 mL
Finely grated ginger root	1 tbsp.	15 mL
Fresh, thin Chinese-style egg noodles, soaked in boiling water, drained	3 cups	750 mL
Large egg	1	1
Finely chopped uncooked shrimp (peeled and deveined)	1 cup	250 mL
Thinly sliced fresh shiitake mushrooms	3/4 cup	175 mL
Julienned red pepper	1/2 cup	125 mL
Cornstarch	2 tbsp.	30 mL
Garlic cloves, minced	2	2
Salt	1 tsp.	5 mL
Pepper	1/2 tsp.	2 mL
Fresh spinach leaves, lightly packed, blanched and squeezed dry	3 cups	750 mL
Cooking oil	2 tbsp.	30 mL

Combine first 3 ingredients in a saucepan and bring to a boil. Reduce heat to medium-low and simmer for 5 minutes to blend flavours. Makes about 1/2 cup (125 mL). Set aside.

Cut noodles in half twice and add next 8 ingredients.

Finely chop spinach and add to noodle mixture. Mix well and shape into small patties, using about 2 tbsp. (30 mL) for each.

Heat 1 tbsp. (15 mL) cooking oil in a large frying pan on medium. Cook patties in 2 batches for 2 minutes per side until golden. Serve with plum sauce. Makes about 16 noodle cakes.

1 noodle cake with 2 tsp. (10 mL) plum sauce: 148 Calories; 3.0 g Total Fat (1.2 g Mono, 0.9 g Poly, 0.5 g Sat); 51 mg Cholesterol; 23 g Carbohydrate; 2 g Fibre; 7 g Protein; 181 mg Sodium

---

ABOUT FRESH CHINESE-STYLE EGG NOODLES
Fresh Asian egg noodles can be found in the produce section of many large supermarkets. Various kinds of noodles are used in several of the continent's cultures; they can be steamed, stir-fried or deep-fried, among other uses, and they are eaten hot or cold at any time of day.

MAKE AHEAD
Make noodle cakes and refrigerate for up to one day. Reheat in 375°F (190°C) oven for about 15 minutes until heated through.

Partners in the sublime. Golden noodle cakes, with lightly crisped edges and an intriguing medley of shrimp and vegetable morsels, meet a tangy, bold plum sauce with a slight ginger bite.

Char Siu Pancake Rolls

Large eggs	2	2
All-purpose flour	3/4 cup	175 mL
Water	3/4 cup	175 mL
Cooking oil	1 tbsp.	15 mL
Sesame oil	2 tsp.	10 mL
Pea shoots, chopped	2 cups	500 mL
Chopped char siu (see How To, below)	1 1/2 cups	375 mL
Chopped fresh chives	1/2 cup	125 mL
Hoisin sauce	2 tbsp.	30 mL
Finely grated ginger root	2 tsp.	10 mL
Garlic cloves, minced	2	2
All purpose flour	1 tbsp.	15 mL
Water	1 tbsp.	15 mL
Sesame oil	1 tbsp.	15 mL

Process first 4 ingredients in a blender or food processor until smooth and let stand for 1 hour. Heat a medium, non-stick frying pan on medium and spray with cooking spray. Pour about 1/4 cup (60 mL) batter into the pan, quickly tilting pan to ensure entire bottom is covered. Cook for 1 minute until edges are dry and centre is no longer shiny. Repeat steps and set finished pancakes aside. Makes about 6 pancakes.

Heat sesame oil in a large frying pan on medium. Add next 6 ingredients and cook for 5 minutes until heated through.

Stir flour and water together to make a paste. Spoon filling along centre of each pancake. Fold sides over filling. Brush top edge with paste. Roll up from bottom to enclose and press to seal.

Heat sesame oil in a large frying pan on medium-high. Cook rolls for 2 minutes per side until browned. Transfer to a paper towel-lined plate to absorb excess oil. Cut rolls in half diagonally to serve. Makes 12 rolls.

1 roll: 138 Calories; 7.3 g Total Fat (1.0 g Mono, 0.5 g Poly, 0.6 g Sat); 35 mg Cholesterol; 16 g Carbohydrate; trace Fibre; 3 g Protein; 102 mg Sodium

ABOUT CHAR SIU (shar-SHOO)
Char siu, or Chinese barbecued pork, is traditionally made from pork seasoned with a blend of sweet and salty ingredients. Char siu and prepared char siu sauce can be found at Asian markets.

HOW TO MAKE CHAR SIU
To make your own char siu, marinate pork tenderloin in purchased char siu sauce for one hour in the refrigerator. Bake on a greased wire rack set in a baking sheet in a 450°F (230°C) oven for 25 to 30 minutes, brushing with more sauce once or twice, until a meat thermometer inserted into pork reads 160°F (70°C).

GARNISH
fresh chives

Traditional flavours and modern presentation rolled into one. Golden pancakes, Chinese barbecued pork and pea shoots come together in harmony. Serve with a light floral tea such as jasmine or a more robustly flavoured tea such as po lei to add another lovely note.

Black Bean Chicken Wings

Chicken drumettes (about 24)	2 lbs.	900 g
Water	4 cups	1 L
Small onion, quartered	1	1
Star anise	3	3
Whole black peppercorns	6	6
Brown sugar, packed	1/4 cup	60 mL
Thick black bean sauce	2 tbsp.	30 mL
Chinese rice wine	2 tbsp.	30 mL
Garlic cloves, minced	2	2
Finely grated ginger root	1 tsp.	5 mL
Chili paste (sambal oelek)	1/2 tsp.	2 mL
Cooking oil	1 tbsp.	15 mL

Remove ends of drumettes with a sharp knife (see How To, page 212). Push meat up toward thick end to expose bone.

Put drumettes and next 4 ingredients into a wok or large frying pan. Bring to a boil, reduce heat to medium-low and simmer for 15 minutes until chicken is no longer pink inside (see Why To, below). Remove chicken. Discard remaining contents of wok, reserving 1/2 cup (125 mL) cooking liquid.

Combine cooking liquid and next 6 ingredients and set aside. Wipe wok dry and heat on medium-high.

Add cooking oil. Add chicken and stir-fry for 5 minutes until browned. Add black bean mixture and stir-fry for 5 minutes until sauce is reduced and chicken is glazed. Makes 24 drumettes.

2 drumettes: 204 Calories; 13.3 g Total Fat (0.7 g Mono, 0.4 g Poly, 3.3 g Sat); 57 mg Cholesterol; 5 g Carbohydrate; trace Fibre; 14 g Protein; 102 mg Sodium

ABOUT STAR ANISE
This star-shaped pod comes from small evergreen trees native to China. Star anise's pungent licorice-like flavour is commonly used to flavour teas and liqueurs and is a key ingredient in Vietnamese pho soup and Chinese five-spice powder.

WHY TO
Cooking the wings in water reduces the fat and makes preparation easier. As an added bonus, you can use the excess poaching liquid as a chicken broth in other recipes.

GARNISH
blanched pea shoots, drizzled with chili oil

Eastern flavours meet Western presentation.
The tawny-glazed drummettes look lovely atop
a bed of vibrant pea shoots.
A drizzle of chili oil awakens the palate.

Stir-Fried Vegetables
in Black Bean Sauce

Cooking oil	1 tbsp.	15 mL
Thinly sliced carrot	1 cup	250 mL
Finely grated ginger root	2 tsp.	10 mL
Garlic cloves, minced	2	2
Can of cut baby corn, blanched (see Why To, below)	14 oz.	398 mL
Can of straw mushrooms, blanched (see Why To, below)	14 oz.	398 mL
Snow peas, trimmed	1 cup	250 mL
Thinly sliced water chestnuts	1/3 cup	75 mL
Vegetable broth	1 cup	250 mL
Thick black bean sauce	3 tbsp.	50 mL
Cornstarch	2 tbsp.	30 mL
Soy sauce	1 tbsp.	15 mL
Pepper	1/4 tsp.	1 mL

Heat a wok or large frying pan on medium-high. Add cooking oil. Add next 3 ingredients and stir-fry for 3 minutes until carrot starts to soften. Add next 4 ingredients and stir-fry for 3 minutes until snow peas start to soften.

Stir remaining 5 ingredients until smooth. Add to wok and stir for 3 minutes until bubbling and thickened and vegetables are tender-crisp. Makes about 5 cups (1.25 L).

1/2 cup (125 mL): 93 Calories; 2.4 g Total Fat (1.1 g Mono, 0.8 g Poly, 0.2 g Sat); 0 mg Cholesterol; 18 g Carbohydrate; 3 g Fibre; 3 g Protein; 395 mg Sodium

ABOUT WATER CHESTNUTS
These may resemble chestnuts, but they're actually tubers from a water plant indigenous to Southeast Asia. The white flesh is both crunchy and juicy and imparts a slightly sweet taste. Water chestnuts' ability to retain their crunchy consistency makes them a preferred ingredient for stir-fries.

WHY TO
Blanching the baby corn and straw mushrooms for one to two minutes helps get rid of the "tinny" taste.

MAKE AHEAD
Prepare and refrigerate the vegetables up to several hours in advance. To ensure that the vegetables reach the tender-crisp stage all at the same time, it's important to have them prepped and at-the-ready before you start cooking.

GARNISH
carrot flowers

Vivid colours and pleasing textures unite.
Tender-crisp mixed vegetables catch the eye,
while a flavourful black bean sauce adds
the perfect complement.

Spicy Long Beans

Chinese rice wine	2 tbsp.	30 mL
Soy sauce	1 tbsp.	15 mL
Hoisin sauce	2 tsp.	10 mL
Liquid honey	1 tsp.	5 mL
Finely chopped small red chili peppers (see Tip, page 148)	1/2 tsp.	2 mL
Sesame oil	1 tbsp.	15 mL
Chopped long beans (3 inch, 7.5 cm, pieces)	3 cups	750 mL
Finely grated ginger root	2 tsp.	10 mL
Garlic cloves, minced	2	2
Water	1/3 cup	75 mL
Sesame seeds, toasted (see Tip, page 128)	2 tsp.	10 mL

Combine first 5 ingredients.

Heat a wok or large frying pan on medium-high. Add sesame oil. Add next 3 ingredients and stir-fry for 2 minutes.

Add water and cook, covered, for 5 minutes until beans are tender.

Add soy sauce mixture and stir-fry for 1 minute until beans are glazed and coated. Sprinkle with sesame seeds and stir. Makes about 1 3/4 cups (425 mL).

1/2 cup (125 mL): 256 Calories; 5.7 g Total Fat (0.1 g Mono, 0.3 g Poly, 0.8 g Sat); 0 mg Cholesterol; 38 g Carbohydrate; 6 g Fibre; 14 g Protein; 501 mg Sodium

ABOUT LONG BEANS
Chinese long beans, or yard-long beans, are very similar to green beans in both colour and taste, but as the name implies, they're much longer! These beans are a vibrant standout in many Asian dishes. Thin, young beans are sweetest.

ABOUT YIN AND YANG
A pervasive Chinese principle, also prevalent in cooking, is yin and yang—achieving balance through juxtapositions of flavours and textures, hot and cold and so on. If you want to hold to tradition, consider leaving out or increasing the chilies, depending on the level of heat in accompanying dishes.

Simply fresh, a delight to share. Try this as an accompaniment to heartier dishes. The fiery red of the finely chopped pepper adds contrast to the cool hue of the beans.

Sweet-and-Sour Chicken

Cornstarch	1/4 cup	60 mL
All-purpose flour	2 tbsp.	30 mL
Baking powder	1/4 tsp.	1 mL
Salt	1/4 tsp.	1 mL
Boneless, skinless chicken breast halves, patted dry, cut into 1 inch (2.5 cm) pieces	1 lb.	454 g
Cooking oil	3 cups	750 mL
Brown sugar, packed	2/3 cup	150 mL
Rice vinegar	1/2 cup	125 mL
Soy sauce	2 tbsp.	30 mL
Tomato paste	2 tbsp.	30 mL
Cornstarch	2 tsp.	10 mL
Cooking oil	1 tbsp.	15 mL
Thinly sliced red pepper	1 cup	250 mL
Sliced water chestnuts	1/2 cup	125 mL
Chopped green onion (1 inch, 2.5 cm pieces)	1/3 cup	75 mL
Garlic cloves, minced	2	2

Combine first 4 ingredients in a large resealable freezer bag. Add chicken and toss until coated.

Heat cooking oil in a large frying pan on medium (see Tip, below). Add chicken, a few pieces at a time, and shallow-fry for 3 minutes, turning occasionally, until golden. Transfer to a paper towel-lined plate to drain.

Combine next 5 ingredients and set aside.

Heat a wok or large frying pan on medium-high. Add cooking oil. Add remaining 4 ingredients and stir-fry for 2 minutes until red pepper is tender-crisp. Stir in vinegar mixture until thickened. Add chicken and stir until coated. Makes about 4 cups (1 L).

1/2 cup (125 mL): 268 Calories; 11.9 g Total Fat (6.5 g Mono, 3.4 g Poly, 1.0 g Sat); 33 mg Cholesterol; 27 g Carbohydrate; 1 g Fibre; 14 g Protein; 451 mg Sodium

TIP
Keep your fried foods crisp, rather than greasy, with properly heated oil that has reached 350 – 375°F (170 – 190°C).
The easiest way to test the temperature is to use a deep-fry thermometer. If you don't have a thermometer, try either of the following:

- Insert the tip of a wooden spoon. If the oil around it bubbles, the temperature is right.
- Toss in a small piece of bread. If it sizzles and turns brown within 1 minute, the oil is ready.

An **authentic-tasting,** familiar favourite. To entice the less adventurous, place this dish among more **exotic** Chinese fare. The distinctly **sweet and sour** flavours of the sauce go well with rice.

Chicken and Vegetables
in Lettuce Cups

Sesame oil	1 tbsp.	15 mL
Diced celery	1/2 cup	125 mL
Chinese dried mushrooms, rehydrated, diced (see Tip, page 84)	8	8
Lean ground chicken	1/2 lb.	225 g
Chopped water chestnuts	1/2 cup	125 mL
Diced red pepper	1/2 cup	125 mL
Chopped green onion	1/4 cup	60 mL
Prepared chicken broth	1/4 cup	60 mL
Chinese rice wine	3 tbsp.	50 mL
Soy sauce	2 tbsp.	30 mL
Hoisin sauce	1 tbsp.	15 mL
Water	1 tbsp.	15 mL
Cornstarch	2 tsp.	10 mL
Pepper	1/4 tsp.	1 mL

Butter lettuce leaves (see Tip, below)

Heat a wok or large frying pan on medium-high. Add sesame oil. Add celery and mushrooms and stir-fry for 3 minutes until celery starts to soften.

Add chicken and stir-fry for 5 minutes until no longer pink.

Add next 3 ingredients and stir-fry for 1 minute.

Stir next 7 ingredients until smooth and add to wok. Heat and stir until bubbling and thickened.

Serve with lettuce leaves. Makes about 4 cups (1 L).

1/2 cup (125 mL): 83 Calories; 4.1 g Total Fat (trace Mono, trace Poly, 0.9 g Sat); 19 mg Cholesterol; 6 g Carbohydrate; 1 g Fibre; 6 g Protein; 420 mg Sodium

ABOUT CHINESE DRIED MUSHROOMS
Dehydrated shiitake mushrooms have a distinct aroma and taste that has no substitute. The stems are usually removed because of their woody texture, but they can be saved to make stock that can be used to add their unique flavour to soups and stir-fries.

ABOUT CANTONESE COOKING
Characterized by the subtle use of sauces, Cantonese cooking is all about preserving the natural flavour of fresh ingredients, using as little cooking and seasoning as possible to achieve the best result.

TIP
Any type of lettuce can be used to make these cups. Endive, for example, would be an interesting choice—its bitterness would contrast well with the filling.

Cradled and captivating. This classic Cantonese dish is sure to invite comment. The flavourful filling is nestled in cool, crisp lettuce beds.

Firecracker Shrimp

Sesame oil	1 tbsp.	15 mL
Uncooked extra-large shrimp (peeled and deveined), tails intact, butterflied	1 lb.	454 g
Finely grated ginger root	2 tsp.	10 mL
Garlic clove, minced	1	1
Chopped yellow pepper	1 cup	250 mL
Chinese rice wine	2 tbsp.	30 mL
Soy sauce	2 tbsp.	30 mL
Sriracha chili sauce	2 tbsp.	30 mL
Finely chopped small red chili peppers (see Tip, page 148)	1 tbsp.	15 mL
Granulated sugar	2 tsp.	10 mL
Rice vinegar	2 tsp.	10 mL
Cornstarch	2 tsp.	10 mL
Water	2 tsp.	10 mL

Heat a wok or large frying pan on medium-high. Add sesame oil. Add next 3 ingredients and stir-fry for 2 minutes until shrimp start to turn pink. Transfer to a bowl and cover to keep warm.

Add yellow pepper to wok and stir-fry for 2 minutes until tender-crisp.

Add next 6 ingredients and stir.

Stir cornstarch and water until smooth and add to wok. Heat and stir until bubbling and thickened. Add shrimp and stir-fry for 1 minute until pink and coated. Makes about 3 1/2 cups (875 mL).

1/2 cup (125 mL): 94 Calories; 2.6 g Total Fat (0.1 g Mono, 0.3 g Poly, 0.4 g Sat); 96 mg Cholesterol; 5 g Carbohydrate; trace Fibre; 11 g Protein; 594 mg Sodium

---

GARNISH
small red chili peppers

ABOUT SICHUAN COOKING
Although this cuisine is made up of many flavours and cooking methods, it is perhaps best known for its pungent, spicy dishes. The Sichuan region, known as a "land of plenty," is rich in natural ingredients and boasts over 5000 unique dishes as a result.

A festival of flavour. A popular dish in Sichuan cooking, chili shrimp can offer an effective contrast to milder dishes and add some heat to the gathering!

Sesame-Glazed Trout

Boiling water	1/2 cup	125 mL
Orange pekoe tea bags	2	2
Rice vinegar	2 tbsp.	30 mL
Soy sauce	2 tbsp.	30 mL
Sesame oil	1 tbsp.	15 mL
Chinese five-spice powder	1 tsp.	5 mL
Steelhead trout fillets	4	4
(4 – 5 oz., 113 – 140 g, each)		
Sesame seeds, toasted (see Tip, page 128)	1/4 cup	60 mL
Liquid honey	2 tbsp.	30 mL
Soy sauce	1 tbsp.	15 mL
Chinese five-spice powder	2 tsp.	10 mL
Sesame oil	1 tsp.	5 mL

Pour boiling water over tea bags in a cup. Chill until cold. Remove tea bags, squeezing out liquid.

Combine next 4 ingredients in a large resealable freezer bag. Add tea and fillets and marinate in the refrigerator for 20 minutes (see Tip, below). Drain and discard marinade. Arrange fillets on a foil-lined baking sheet and pat dry.

Combine remaining 5 ingredients and spread over fillets. Broil 6 inches (15 cm) from heat in oven for 5 to 7 minutes until fish flakes easily when tested with a fork. Makes 4 fillets.

1 fillet: 302 Calories; 15.3 g Total Fat (3.7 g Mono, 1.7 g Poly, 1.8 g Sat); 66 mg Cholesterol; 13 g Carbohydrate; 0 g Fibre; 26 g Protein; 805 mg Sodium

---

GARNISH
sautéed spinach leaves
finely sliced green onion

TIP
Don't leave the fish in the marinade for longer than the recommended time. The tea infuses the mild fish with flavour, but it will also begin to break down the texture if left too long.

MAKE AHEAD
Make and refrigerate both the marinade and sauce up to one day in advance.

Truly honour your guests. Spices and tea add complexity to this delicate fish, while a sweet glaze, flecked with sesame seeds, makes for a memorable dish. Serve on a bed of sautéed greens.

Chinese Clay Pot Beef

Cooking oil	1 tbsp.	15 mL
Boneless beef cross-rib roast, cut into 1 1/2 inch (3.8 cm) cubes	1 1/2 lbs.	680 g
Chopped green onion (2 inch, 5 cm, pieces)	1 1/2 cups	375 mL
Sliced fresh shiitake mushrooms	1 cup	250 mL
Thinly sliced carrot	1 cup	250 mL
Garlic cloves, sliced	3	3
Chinese rice wine	1/2 cup	125 mL
Prepared beef broth	4 cups	1 L
Soy sauce	1/4 cup	60 mL
Star anise	2	2
Cinnamon stick (4 inches, 10 cm)	1	1
Piece of ginger root (2 inch, 5 cm, length), sliced	1	1
Salt	1 tsp.	5 mL
Bean thread noodles	4 oz.	113 g
Cornstarch	2 tbsp.	30 mL
Water	2 tbsp.	30 mL
Baby bok choy, halved lengthwise	6	6

Heat cooking oil in a large frying pan on medium-high. Add beef and cook until browned. Transfer with a slotted spoon to a 3 1/2 to 4 quart (3 1/2 to 4 L) slow cooker.

Add next 4 ingredients to pan and stir-fry for 2 minutes until browned.

Add rice wine and stir for 1 minute, scraping any brown bits from bottom of pan. Transfer vegetables to slow cooker.

Stir in next 6 ingredients. Cook, covered, on Low for 8 to 10 hours or on High for 4 to 5 hours. Discard star anise, cinnamon stick and ginger. Skim and discard any fat.

Put noodles into a bowl and cover with hot water. Let stand for 10 minutes until softened. Drain.

Stir cornstarch and water until smooth. Add noodles, cornstarch mixture and bok choy to slow cooker and stir. Cook on High, covered, for 20 minutes until slightly thickened. Makes about 11 1/2 cups (2.9 L).

1 cup (250 mL): 314 Calories; 18.2 g Total Fat (7.9 g Mono, 1.2 g Poly, 7.0 g Sat); 39 mg Cholesterol; 21 g Carbohydrate; 4 g Fibre; 15 g Protein; 1315 mg Sodium

Bring close friends closer. Earthy mushrooms lend even more appeal to this one-dish meal of anise-scented broth with tender meat, bean thread noodles, tender-crisp greens and sweet carrots.

Almond Jellies
With Lychee and Mango

Water	1 cup	250 mL
Granulated sugar	1/4 cup	60 mL
Envelope of unflavoured gelatin (about 1 tbsp, 15 mL)	1/4 oz	7 g
Evaporated milk	1 cup	250 mL
Almond extract	1 tsp.	5 mL
Finely diced lychee	1/3 cup	75 mL
Finely diced mango	1/3 cup	75 mL

Stir water and sugar in a saucepan until sugar is dissolved. Sprinkle with gelatin and let stand for 1 minute. Heat and stir on medium-low until gelatin is dissolved. Stir in milk and extract. Pour into small glasses or serving dishes and chill for 2 hours until firm.

Combine lychee and mango and spoon over jellies. Serves 6.

1 serving: 105 Calories; 2.7 g Total Fat (0.6 g Mono, 0.1 g Poly, 2.0 g Sat); 13 mg Cholesterol; 16 g Carbohydrate; trace Fibre; 4 g Protein; 43 mg Sodium

GARNISH
sprigs of mint

Small wonders. Silky smooth jellies with a luscious lychee and mango topping—splendour that captures the attention, spoonfuls that dance on the tongue.

No matter what you serve your guests, the colour and aroma of India's wealth of spices will entice their senses—a virtually infinite array of tastes and textures can be drawn from these spices, used in every dish. Set the stage for an opulent Indian meal by draping brilliant swathes of raspberry or turquoise fabric over your table, contrasting with bunches of fresh marigolds. Enhance the enchantment with a cluster of pillar candles.

Indian

Spices Abound

Peas and Paneer in Pepper Boats

Baby bell peppers (red and yellow), halved lengthwise	6	6
Ghee	1 tbsp.	15 mL
Cumin seed	2 tsp.	10 mL
Chopped onion	1/2 cup	125 mL
Mild curry paste	1 tbsp.	15 mL
Salt	1/2 tsp.	2 mL
Pepper	1/4 tsp.	1 mL
Diced paneer (1/4 inch, 6 mm, pieces)	1 cup	250 mL
Frozen peas, thawed	1 cup	250 mL
Balkan-style yogurt	1/3 cup	75 mL
Chopped fresh mint	1 tbsp.	15 mL

Arrange bell peppers, cut-side up, on a greased baking sheet. Broil on top rack in oven for 5 minutes until starting to soften. Set aside.

Heat ghee in a frying pan on medium-high. Add cumin seed and stir for 30 seconds until toasted. Add next 4 ingredients and cook for 3 minutes until onion is softened.

Add paneer and peas and stir to coat. Add yogurt and stir until hot. Remove from heat (see Tip, below) and stir in mint. Spoon paneer mixture into bell pepper halves. Makes 12 peppers.

1 pepper: 106 Calories; 6.6 g Total Fat (0.1 g Mono, 0.1 g Poly, 4.1 g Sat); 22 mg Cholesterol; 6 g Carbohydrate; 2 g Fibre; 6 g Protein; 174 mg Sodium

ABOUT GHEE (GEE)
This versatile variation of clarified butter is created by simmering butter until it is infused with a nutty aroma. Ghee doesn't burn as quickly as regular butter, making it a useful ingredient for high-heat cooking such as sautéing or frying. While ghee is a staple of many Indian dishes, most premium ghee is produced in Holland.

TIP
If overheated, yogurt will curdle. When you add it to hot dishes, do so gradually or only cook until heated through.

GARNISH
sprigs of mint
chopped red pepper

Stir the senses. Fragrant cumin and mint are infused into a paneer and pea blend, cupped in vibrant baby bell peppers.

Vegetable Pakoras

Chickpea flour	3/4 cup	175 mL
All-purpose flour	1/2 cup	125 mL
Cumin seed	1 tbsp.	15 mL
Ground coriander	1 tsp.	5 mL
Baking soda	1/2 tsp.	2 mL
Garam masala	1/2 tsp.	2 mL
Salt	1/2 tsp.	2 mL
Cayenne pepper	1/8 tsp.	0.5 mL
Water	1 cup	250 mL
Chopped red pepper	1 cup	250 mL
Small cauliflower florets	1 cup	250 mL
Chopped onion	1/2 cup	125 mL
Diced cooked potato	1/2 cup	125 mL
Frozen peas, thawed	1/2 cup	125 mL
Frozen kernel corn, thawed	1/2 cup	125 mL
Chopped fresh cilantro	1 tbsp.	15 mL
Cooking oil	3 cups	750 mL

Salt, sprinkle

Combine first 8 ingredients in a medium bowl. Add water and whisk until smooth.

Add next 7 ingredients and stir until coated.

Heat cooking oil in a large frying pan on medium-high (see Tip, page 26). Drop 8 portions of vegetable mixture into oil, using a rounded tablespoon (15 mL) for each. Shallow-fry for 2 minutes per side until browned. Transfer to paper towels to drain.

While pakoras are still hot, sprinkle with salt. Repeat steps (see Tip, below). Serve with mango chutney or coriander chutney mixed with yogurt. Makes about 40 pakoras.

1 pakora: 51 Calories; 3.9 g Total Fat (2.1 g Mono, 1.1 g Poly, 0.3 g Sat); 0 mg Cholesterol; 4 g Carbohydrate; 1 g Fibre; 1 g Protein; 52 mg Sodium

---

GARNISH
red pepper slices

ABOUT CHICKPEA FLOUR
Also known as *besan*, chickpea flour can be found in Indian and other Asian markets, as well as health food stores. It provides a distinctive flavour that all-purpose flour cannot, as well as being a gluten-free alternative.

TIP
Allow the frying oil to come back up to temperature between batches.

MAKE AHEAD
Make and refrigerate up to two days in advance. Reheat in 375°F (190°C) oven for 10 minutes until hot.

Bright vegetable morsels peek through these light and crispy spiced fritters, inviting guests to have a taste. Scrumptious on their own, or dipped into waiting bowls of chutney.

Vegetable Samosas
With Coriander Sesame Chutney

Ghee	2 tsp.	10 mL
Chopped onion	1/2 cup	125 mL
Finely grated ginger root	1 1/2 tsp.	7 mL
Chopped cooked potato	1 3/4 cups	425 mL
Frozen peas, thawed	1/3 cup	75 mL
Finely chopped fresh cilantro	2 tsp.	10 mL
Lemon juice	2 tsp.	10 mL
Brown mustard seed, toasted	1 tsp.	5 mL
(see Tip, page 128)		
Garam masala	1 tsp.	5 mL
Salt	1/2 tsp.	2 mL
Cayenne pepper	1/4 tsp.	1 mL
Pastry for 2 crust 9 inch (22 cm) pie		
Large egg, fork-beaten	1	1
Balkan-style yogurt	1/3 cup	75 mL
Prepared coriander chutney	2 tbsp.	30 mL
Tahini	1 tbsp.	15 mL

Heat ghee in a frying pan on medium-high. Add onion and ginger and cook for 5 minutes until onion is softened.

Stir in next 8 ingredients and cool.

Divide pastry into 6 portions. Roll out each portion into a 6 inch (15 cm) circle and cut circles in half. Spoon filling onto each semicircle (see How To, page 212). Brush edges with egg. Fold over and seal. Arrange on a greased baking sheet and bake in a 400°F (205°C) oven for 20 minutes until golden.

Combine remaining 3 ingredients and serve with samosas. Makes about 1/2 cup (125 mL) yogurt mixture and 12 samosas.

1 samosa with 2 tsp. (10 mL) yogurt mixture: 214 Calories; 11.5 g Total Fat (0.5 g Mono, 0.4 g Poly, 4.8 g Sat); 26 mg Cholesterol; 24 g Carbohydrate; 1 g Fibre; 3 g Protein; 349 mg Sodium

---

MAKE AHEAD
Make samosas, but do not bake. Freeze and store them in an airtight container, or keep refrigerated for up to one day. When ready to serve, arrange on a greased baking sheet and bake in a 400°F (205°) oven for 20 minutes until golden and filling is hot.

A mildly spiced potato and pea fusion wrapped in soft, golden pastry. Served with smooth coriander chutney sauce for dipping, it's a divine pairing.

Tamarind Vegetable Curry

Ingredient	Imperial	Metric
Ghee	2 tbsp.	30 mL
Brown mustard seed	1 tsp.	5 mL
Cumin seed	1 tsp.	5 mL
Chopped onion	1 1/2 cups	375 mL
Finely grated ginger root	2 tbsp.	30 mL
Garlic cloves, minced	4	4
Hot curry paste	2 tbsp.	30 mL
Cubed peeled orange-fleshed sweet potato (1/2 inch, 12 mm, pieces)	1 1/2 cups	375 mL
Cubed butternut squash (1/2 inch, 12 mm, pieces)	1 cup	250 mL
Chopped fresh green beans	2 cups	500 mL
Tamarind liquid (see How To, page 212)	3/4 cup	175 mL
Brown sugar, packed	3 tbsp.	50 mL
Salt	1 tsp.	5 mL
Pepper	1/2 tsp.	2 mL

Heat ghee in a frying pan on medium. Add mustard and cumin seed and stir for 15 seconds until mustard seed pops (see Why To, below).

Add next 3 ingredients and cook for 5 minutes until onion is softened.

Add curry paste and stir for 1 minute. Add sweet potato and squash. Cook for 10 minutes, stirring occasionally, until potato starts to brown.

Add remaining 5 ingredients and bring to a boil. Cook, covered, for 8 minutes until potato and squash are tender. Makes about 4 1/2 cups (1.1 L).

1/2 cup (125 mL): 133 Calories; 4.3 g Total Fat (0.1 g Mono, 0.1 g Poly, 2.3 g Sat); 5 mg Cholesterol; 23 g Carbohydrate; 3 g Fibre; 2 g Protein; 424 mg Sodium

---

WHY TO
The technique of dropping spices into hot oil is known as *baghaar*. It changes the nature of the spices by concentrating their flavours.

ABOUT THICKENING INDIAN DISHES
Flour is almost never used as a thickening agent in Indian cooking. Instead, ingredients such as vegetables and yogurt add body to sauces.

This **sweet** and **tangy** dish is reminiscent of chutney,
rich with **curry** and **mustard seed**.
A **hot** and **sour** side that's right at home in
a **lavish spread** of Indian dishes.

Smashed Aloo

Multicoloured baby potatoes	1 lb.	454 g
Small onion, halved	1	1
Curry powder	1 tsp.	5 mL
Butter, melted	2 tbsp.	30 mL
Garam masala	1/2 tsp.	2 mL
Ground coriander	1/2 tsp.	2 mL
Ground cumin	1/2 tsp.	2 mL
Salt	1/8 tsp.	0.5 mL
Garam masala	1/4 tsp.	1 mL

Cook first 3 ingredients in a large saucepan of boiling salted water on medium for 20 minutes until potatoes are tender. Drain and discard onion. Arrange potatoes in a single layer on a greased baking sheet. Press potatoes with bottom of a cup or bowl until flattened.

Combine next 5 ingredients and brush over potatoes. Broil on top rack in oven for 10 minutes until browned and crisp.

Sprinkle with garam masala. Makes about 20 smashed potatoes.

1 smashed potato: 24 Calories; 1.2 g Total Fat (0.3 g Mono, trace Poly, 0.7 g Sat); 3 mg Cholesterol; 3 g Carbohydrate; trace Fibre; trace Protein; 31 mg Sodium

---

ABOUT ALOO
Aloo, or potatoes, take on an important role in Indian cooking. All sorts of recipe variations abound.

MAKE AHEAD
Boil potatoes a day ahead and proceed with the remaining steps the next day.

The delightful presentation of this versatile potato dish is bound to stir excitement. Flattened baby potatoes, dusted with curry spices, are buttery and tender.

Chickpea and Cauliflower Curry

Butter	1 tbsp.	15 mL
Cauliflower florets	2 cups	500 mL
Chopped onion	1 cup	250 mL
Finely grated ginger root	2 tsp.	10 mL
Ground coriander	1 tsp.	5 mL
Ground cumin	1 tsp.	5 mL
Dried crushed chilies	1/4 tsp.	1 mL
Salt	1/4 tsp.	1 mL
Cayenne pepper	1/4 tsp.	1 mL
Can of chickpeas (garbanzo beans), rinsed and drained	19 oz.	540 mL
Can of diced tomatoes, drained	14 oz.	398 mL
Prepared vegetable broth	1/2 cup	125 mL

Melt butter in a large saucepan on medium. Add cauliflower and onion and cook for 10 minutes, stirring often, until onion is golden.

Add next 6 ingredients and stir for 1 minute.

Add remaining 3 ingredients and reduce heat to medium-low. Simmer, covered, for 10 minutes until cauliflower is tender. Makes about 4 cups (1 L).

1/2 cup (125 mL): 99 Calories; 2.7 g Total Fat (0.6 g Mono, 0.6 g Poly, 0.9 g Sat); 4 mg Cholesterol; 15 g Carbohydrate; 4 g Fibre; 4 g Protein; 309 mg Sodium

---

GARNISH
chopped fresh cilantro

Sweetly spiced with ginger heat, scented with cumin and coriander—a rich, colourful vegetable dish with a smattering of cilantro. Ideal for ladling over steaming basmati rice.

Spicy Bean Dal

Dried Indian black beans (sabat urad), soaked overnight and drained	1 cup	250 mL
Dried red kidney beans, soaked overnight and drained	1 cup	250 mL
Water	10 cups	2.5 L
Can of petite diced tomatoes, drained	19 oz.	540 g
Whipping cream	1/4 cup	60 mL
Ghee	2 tbsp.	30 mL
Finely grated ginger root	1 tbsp.	15 mL
Garlic cloves, minced	3	3
Garam masala	2 tsp.	10 mL
Salt	1 tsp.	5 mL
Cayenne pepper	1/2 tsp.	2 mL
Ghee	2 tbsp.	30 mL
Sliced onion	3/4 cup	175 mL
Cayenne pepper, sprinkle		

Combine beans and water in a Dutch oven and bring to a boil. Simmer, covered, on medium-low for 3 hours until tender. Drain beans and mash half (see Why To, below). Return to pot.

Add tomatoes and cream. Keep warm on low.

Heat ghee in a frying pan on medium. Add next 5 ingredients and stir for 1 minute until fragrant. Stir into bean mixture and transfer to a serving dish. Cover to keep warm.

Heat ghee in pan on medium-high. Add onion and cook for 5 minutes, stirring occasionally, until browned and crispy. Spoon over bean mixture and sprinkle with cayenne. Makes about 6 cups (1.5 L).

1/2 cup (125 mL): 180 Calories; 7.1 g Total Fat (0.5 g Mono, 0.1 g Poly, 4.2 g Sat); 15 mg Cholesterol; 21 g Carbohydrate; 5 g Fibre; 7 g Protein; 348 mg Sodium

ABOUT DRIED INDIAN BLACK BEANS
Also known as *sabat urad*, Indian black beans are one of the most prominent beans used for making dals. This recipe uses whole beans, but they are also sold split. You can find these beans in Indian grocery stores.

WHY TO
Dals are bean- or lentil-based dishes, combining whole and mashed beans to provide a creamy texture.

MAKE AHEAD
Cook beans, then cool and refrigerate up to two days in advance.

GARNISH
chopped cilantro

A true crowd-pleaser. This creamy bean curry is earthy, rich and touched with spice, while crisped onions provide sweet contrast. Perfectly suited for generous scoops on naan and roti.

Chicken Biryani

Ingredient	Imperial	Metric
Ghee	1 tbsp.	15 mL
Boneless, skinless chicken thighs, cut into bite-sized pieces	1 lb.	454 g
Salt, sprinkle		
Pepper, sprinkle		
Ghee	1 tbsp.	15 mL
Chopped onion	1 cup	250 mL
Garlic cloves, minced	2	2
Finely grated ginger root	1 tsp.	5 mL
Basmati rice	1 1/2 cups	375 mL
Mild curry paste	1 tbsp.	15 mL
Cinnamon stick (4 inches, 10 cm)	1	1
Dried crushed chilies	1/2 tsp.	2 mL
Saffron threads	1/2 tsp.	2 mL
Whole green cardamom, bruised	3	3
Prepared chicken broth	2 1/2 cups	625 mL
Ghee	2 tsp.	10 mL
Sliced natural almonds	1/4 cup	60 mL
Can of petite diced tomatoes, drained	19 oz.	540 mL

Heat ghee in a Dutch oven on medium-high. Add chicken to pot and sprinkle with salt and pepper. Cook for 5 minutes until no longer pink inside and transfer to a plate.

Add ghee to pot and reduce heat to medium. Add next 3 ingredients and cook for 5 minutes until onion starts to soften. Add rice and stir until coated.

Add next 5 ingredients and stir until fragrant. Add broth and chicken and bring to a boil. Cook, covered, for 15 minutes, without lifting lid, until rice is tender. Remove from heat and let stand for 5 minutes until any liquid is absorbed.

Heat ghee in a frying pan on medium. Add almonds and stir-fry for 3 minutes until starting to brown. Add tomatoes and stir for 1 minute. Spoon rice mixture into a serving dish and top with tomato mixture. Makes about 6 cups (1.5 L).

1 cup (250 mL): 320 Calories; 15.2 g Total Fat (3.8 g Mono, 2.0 g Poly, 5.9 g Sat); 60 mg Cholesterol; 26 g Carbohydrate; 2 g Fibre; 18 g Protein; 973 mg Sodium

ABOUT SAFFRON
Saffron stigmas, or threads, grow from a small purple crocus found in many parts of Europe and Asia. It takes over 14,000 stigmas to produce 1 oz (28 g) of saffron. Fortunately, a small amount of saffron will flavour a large amount of food. Buy whole saffron threads rather than ground to ensure you are getting a top-quality product.

ABOUT BIRYANI
Derived from the Farsi word *birian*, which means "fried or roasted before cooking," biryani is made from rice and meat cooked separately. Often, the rice is fried or roasted before liquid is added. This technique draws a nutty flavour from the rice as well as "sealing" the outside starch layer to keep the grains from sticking to each other.

GARNISH
chopped fresh cilantro
cinnamon sticks

Curried chicken and vividly coloured rice flavoured with **saffron and cilantro,** topped with sweet **tomatoes** and **almonds.** A lovely cinnamon garnish hints at the **spices to come.**

Coconut Chili Halibut

Chopped fresh cilantro	1/4 cup	60 mL
Plain yogurt	1/4 cup	60 mL
Garlic cloves, chopped	4	4
Finely grated ginger root	1 tbsp.	15 mL
Hot curry paste	1 tbsp.	15 mL
Small red chili peppers, chopped (see Tip, page 148)	2	2
Salt	1/2 tsp.	2 mL
Sweetened medium coconut	1/2 cup	125 mL
Chopped pistachios, toasted (see Tip, page 128)	1/4 cup	60 mL
Halibut fillets (4 – 6 oz., 113 – 170 g, each)	4	4

Process first 7 ingredients in a blender or food processor until smooth. Transfer to a small bowl.

Stir in coconut and pistachios.

Arrange fillets on a greased baking sheet and top with coconut mixture. Broil on centre rack in oven for 10 minutes until fish flakes easily with a fork. Makes 4 fillets.

1 fillet: 245 Calories; 10.1 g Total Fat (2.9 g Mono, 2.0 g Poly, 3.7 g Sat); 37 mg Cholesterol; 11 g Carbohydrate; 2 g Fibre; 27 g Protein; 520 mg Sodium

---

GARNISH
shredded coconut, toasted
cilantro leaves
small red chili peppers

Lay it on thick. Moist halibut fillets spiced up with a rich, nutty curry topping make a most appetizing entree. The chili heat is mellowed by sweet coconut and pleasing pistachios.

Butter Chicken

Balkan-style yogurt	1/2 cup	125 mL
Lemon juice	1 tbsp.	15 mL
Garlic cloves, minced	3	3
Finely grated ginger root	1 tbsp.	15 mL
Curry powder	2 tsp.	10 mL
Smoked sweet paprika	2 tsp.	10 mL
Boneless, skinless chicken thighs, halved	1 lb.	454 g
Ghee	1 tbsp.	15 mL
Cumin seed	1 tbsp.	15 mL
Finely chopped onion	1 cup	250 mL
Salt	1/2 tsp.	2 mL
Tomato paste	1/4 cup	60 mL
Prepared chicken broth	1 cup	250 mL
Whipping cream	1/2 cup	125 mL
Whole black cardamom	3	3
Bay leaves	2	2
Cinnamon stick (4 inches, 10 cm)	1	1

Combine first 6 ingredients in a large resealable freezer bag. Add chicken and marinate in the refrigerator for 4 hours. Drain and discard marinade. Arrange chicken on a greased baking sheet and cook in a 500°F (260°C) oven (see Why To, below) for 10 minutes until no longer pink inside.

Heat ghee in a large frying pan on medium-high. Add cumin seed and stir for 30 seconds until toasted. Add onion and salt and reduce heat to medium. Cook for 7 minutes until onion is softened.

Add tomato paste, stirring for 3 minutes until paste is slightly browned.

Add remaining 5 ingredients and stir until smooth. Bring to a boil and reduce heat to medium-low. Simmer for 10 minutes until sauce is thickened. Strain sauce through sieve and return to pan. Discard solids. Add chicken to sauce, stirring until heated through. Makes about 2 cups (500 mL).

1/2 cup (125 mL): 92 Calories; 6.0 g Total Fat (1.7 g Mono, 0.6 g Poly, 2.9 g Sat); 30 mg Cholesterol; 3 g Carbohydrate; 1 g Fibre; 6 g Protein; 197 mg Sodium

GARNISH
unsalted roasted cashews
chopped fresh cilantro

WHY TO
Cooking in a very hot oven helps imitate the effect of the *tandoor*, the clay oven traditionally used to roast the chicken for this dish. The juices are sealed in, resulting in meat that is more tender. The yogurt marinade, in addition to tenderizing, helps protect the skinless chicken in the hot oven.

This rich and enticing dish will likely be familiar to guests, and eagerly anticipated all the more. An accompaniment of hot basmati rice is truly essential for soaking up every drop of decadent sauce.

Kashmiri Lamb Chops

Salt	1/2 tsp.	2 mL
Pepper	1/4 tsp.	1 mL
Racks of lamb (8 ribs each), 1 1/3 lbs., (604 g), separated into 16 chops	2	2
Garam masala	1/2 tsp.	2 mL
Rogan josh sauce	1 cup	250 mL
Plain yogurt	1/4 cup	60 mL
Large Roma (plum) tomatoes, seeded and diced	2	2
Finely chopped red onion	2 tbsp.	30 mL
Chopped fresh mint	2 tbsp.	30 mL

Sprinkle salt and pepper over lamb. Cook on a greased grill on medium for 2 minutes per side until a meat thermometer reads 145°F (63°C) for medium-rare.

Sprinkle with garam masala.

Bring sauce to a boil in a saucepan. Remove from heat and stir in yogurt (see Tip, page 40). Pour into a shallow serving dish and arrange lamb chops over sauce.

Sprinkle with remaining 3 ingredients. Makes 16 lamb chops.

2 lamb chops: 228 Calories; 14.5 g Total Fat (5.3 g Mono, 0.9 g Poly, 5.4 g Sat); 55 mg Cholesterol; 8 g Carbohydrate; 1 g Fibre; 16 g Protein; 560 mg Sodium

ABOUT ROGAN JOSH SAUCE

The traditional rogan josh is a lamb curry dish made with relatively mild Kashmiri chilies and a tomato-based sauce that typically features onions, ginger, yogurt and robust Indian spices. Prepared rogan josh sauce can be found at Indian grocery stores, as well as many larger food stores.

Now for the showstopper. Exotically spiced lamb chops unite traditional flavours with stunning presentation. Sprinklings of mint, red onion and tomato create fresh contrast with the bold rogan josh sauce.

Chai Pistachio Parfaits

Large egg	1	1
Egg yolk (large)	1	1
Chai tea concentrate	1 cup	250 mL
Coconut milk	1/4 cup	60 mL
Granulated sugar	1/4 cup	60 mL
Homogenized milk	1/4 cup	60 mL
Cornstarch	2 tbsp.	30 mL
Cooked basmati rice (about 1/2 cup, 125 mL, uncooked)	1 1/2 cups	375 mL
Chopped pistachios, toasted (see Tip, page 128)	1 cup	250 mL
Shredded coconut, toasted (see Tip, page 128)	1/2 cup	125 mL
Ground cardamom	1/2 tsp.	2 mL

Bring first 7 ingredients to a boil in a saucepan, whisking constantly, until mixture starts to thicken.

Add rice and stir until heated through.

Combine remaining 3 ingredients. Alternate layers of rice pudding and pistachio mixture in 6 glasses, ending with pistachio mixture. Makes 6 parfaits.

1 parfait: 307 Calories; 17.1 g Total Fat (6.1 g Mono, 3.3 g Poly, 6.3 g Sat); 71 mg Cholesterol; 32 g Carbohydrate; 3 g Fibre; 9 g Protein; 51 mg Sodium

ABOUT INDIAN RICE PUDDING

In south and east India, versions of this dessert—also known as *kheer*—are made for festivals, such as Diwali, the Festival of Lights. Typically, nuts and cardamom are used, as well as basmati rice for its texture and fragrance.

Incite murmurs of appreciation. Enchanting rice pudding parfaits are fragrant with cardamom and coconut. Pistachio layers give a distinctly sophisticated look to this elegant dessert.

The essence of Japanese cuisine is in its pure flavours and minimalist aesthetics. Traditional dishes are prepared with a light hand, enhancing the natural flavours of fresh, seasonal ingredients, and presented with exquisite simplicity. Create a serene ambiance akin to a tea ceremony by gathering guests around a low table, seated on tatami mats for a tranquil Japanese meal. Keep embellishments to a minimum: delicate cherry blossoms in a slender black vase.

Japanese

Edible Art

Shichimi Edamame

Frozen unshelled edamame	1/2 lb.	225 g
Mirin	2 tbsp.	30 mL
Soy sauce	2 tbsp.	30 mL
Japanese seven-spice blend	1/2 tsp.	2 mL

Cook edamame in a large saucepan of boiling salted water for 5 minutes. Drain well.

Combine next 3 ingredients in a large frying pan on medium. Heat and stir for 4 minutes until slightly reduced. Add edamame and stir until coated. Makes about 2 cups (500 mL).

1/2 cup (125 mL): 98 Calories; 2.3 g Total Fat (0 g Mono, 0 g Poly, 0 g Sat); 0 mg Cholesterol; 10 g Carbohydrate; 3 g Fibre; 7 g Protein; 680 mg Sodium

ABOUT EDAMAME (eh-dah-MAH-meh)
Although the name sounds exotic, *edamame* is simply the Japanese name for fresh soybeans. A popular snack on their own or a welcome addition to many recipes, edamame are regarded for their plump size and nutty flavour.

SERVING SUGGESTION
Try serving individual bowls of edamame as an appetizer with shrimp or tempura.

A pleasing appetizer coated in a delectable, spicy glaze—such fun. Guests new to the toothsome experience of edamame won't soon forget how marvellously addictive they are.

Dynamite Vegetable Maki

Water	2 1/4 cups	550 mL
Short-grain white rice, rinsed and drained	1 1/2 cups	375 mL
Rice vinegar	3 tbsp.	50 mL
Granulated sugar	2 tbsp.	30 mL
Salt	1 tsp.	15 mL
Nori sheets	4	4
Nori sheets	4	4
Large avocado, cut into 1/4 inch (6 mm) strips	1	1
Julienned English cucumber	1 cup	250 mL
Julienned carrot	1/2 cup	125 mL
Mayonnaise	1 cup	250 mL
Granulated sugar	2 tbsp.	30 mL
Sesame oil	2 tsp.	10 mL
Sriracha chili sauce	2 tsp.	10 mL

Bring water and rice to a boil in a medium saucepan. Reduce heat to medium-low and simmer, covered, for 12 minutes, without lifting lid, until rice is tender and liquid is absorbed. Remove from heat and let stand, covered, for 10 minutes. Transfer to a bowl.

Stir next 3 ingredients until sugar is dissolved. Add to rice and stir. Let stand until cool.

Place 1 nori sheet on work surface. Spread 1 cup (250 mL) rice over nori sheet, leaving a 1 inch (2.5 cm) border on top edge. Roll up tightly from bottom. Repeat with 3 more nori sheets and remaining rice. Wrap rolls with plastic wrap and chill for at least 2 hours. Cut each roll lengthwise into 4 quarters.

Lay 1 nori sheet on work surface. Place 2 quarters, cut-side down, on bottom edge of nori sheet (see How To, page 213). Arrange next 3 ingredients along centre of rolls. Arrange remaining 2 rice roll quarters on top, cut-side up. Dampen top edge of nori sheet with a little water. Roll up tightly from bottom. Wrap with plastic wrap. Repeat steps. Chill for 1 hour and cut each roll into 8 slices.

Combine remaining 4 ingredients and serve with maki. Makes about 32 maki and 1 1/4 cups (300 mL) sauce.

1 maki with 2 tsp. (10 mL) sauce: 97 Calories; 6.8 g Total Fat (0.6 g Mono, 0.1 g Poly, 0.9 g Sat); 3 mg Cholesterol; 8 g Carbohydrate; 1 g Fibre; 1 g Protein; 131 mg Sodium

MAKE AHEAD
Sushi can be made a few hours in advance. Wrap whole rolls in plastic wrap and chill. Slice just before serving.

Delicate sushi squares appear intricate, yet are deceptively straightforward. The sauce's gentle heat offers a delightful contrast.

Sushi Treasures

Chopped king crab leg meat, lightly packed	1/2 cup	125 mL
Mayonnaise	4 tsp.	20 mL
Grated lemon zest	1/2 tsp.	2 mL
Coarsely ground pepper	1/4 tsp.	1 mL
Water	1/2 cup	125 mL
Short-grain white rice, rinsed and drained	1/3 cup	75 mL
Rice vinegar	1 tbsp.	15 mL
Granulated sugar	1 tsp.	5 mL
Salt	1/4 tsp.	1 mL
Boiling water	4 cups	1 L
Instant dashi granules	1/2 tsp.	2 mL
Deep-fried tofu puffs, halved	8	8
Finely chopped fresh chives	2 tsp.	10 mL
Grated lemon zest	1 tsp.	5 mL

Combine first 4 ingredients, cover and chill.

Bring water and rice to a boil in a small saucepan. Reduce heat to medium-low and simmer, covered, for 12 minutes, without lifting lid, until rice is tender and liquid is absorbed. Remove from heat and let stand, covered, for 10 minutes. Transfer to a bowl.

Stir next 3 ingredients until sugar is dissolved. Stir into rice and cool.

Combine boiling water and dashi granules in a large bowl. Add tofu puffs and soak for 5 minutes. Drain and squeeze dry.

Fill with rice mixture and top with crab mixture. Arrange on a serving plate. Sprinkle with chives and lemon zest. Makes 16 pieces.

1 piece: 42 Calories; 2.1 g Total Fat (trace Mono, trace Poly, 0.3 g Sat); 3 mg Cholesterol; 3 g Carbohydrate; trace Fibre; 3 g Protein; 102 mg Sodium

ABOUT DEEP-FRIED TOFU PUFFS
Tofu is made from the curds extracted from curdled soymilk using a method similar to how cheese is made. Tofu puffs are hollow, deep-fried tofu pieces, a versatile vessel for Asian ingredients. Tofu puffs' unobtrusive flavour makes them adaptable to many recipes, as they take on the flavours of the ingredients they're cooked with.

MAKE AHEAD
Prepare the pockets and stuff them with rice a couple of hours ahead. Keep covered with plastic wrap and refrigerated. Prepare, cover and refrigerate crab mixture up to one day in advance. Assemble and garnish before serving.

Invoke simple sophistication. Tofu pockets filled with fragrant sticky rice are adorned with a citrusy melange of crab and pepper, transforming them into elegant jewel boxes.

Cucumber Pear Salad

Rice vinegar	1/3 cup	75 mL
Granulated sugar	2 tbsp.	30 mL
Finely grated ginger root	2 tsp.	10 mL
Salt	1/2 tsp.	2 mL
Julienned Asian pear	1 cup	250 mL
Julienned English cucumber	1 cup	250 mL
Julienned carrot	1/4 cup	60 mL
Julienned daikon radish	1/4 cup	60 mL
Julienned red pepper	1/4 cup	60 mL

Stir first 4 ingredients until sugar is dissolved.

Add remaining 5 ingredients and toss. Makes about 2 1/2 cups (625 mL).

1/2 cup (125 mL): 46 Calories; 0.1 g Total Fat (0 g Mono, trace Poly, trace Sat); 0 mg Cholesterol; 12 g Carbohydrate; trace Fibre; 1 g Protein; 240 mg Sodium

ABOUT ASIAN PEARS
The Asian pear is slightly more round than the familiar Bartlett pear, and considerably juicier. Asian pears offer a sweet-and-sour sensation that's similar to pineapple.

ABOUT JAPANESE SALADS
Known as *sunomono*, which means "vinegared things," this style of Japanese salad offers a refreshing contrast to other traditional dishes. *Sunomono* salads are served with main dishes and not as starters.

GARNISH
cucumber slices
carrot flower
red pepper slices

Understated elegance. A refreshing blend of clean cucumber, vegetable matchsticks and crisply sweet Asian pear, all tossed with an aromatic dressing.

Miso Soup
With Shiitake and Squash

Water	4 cups	1 L
Instant dashi granules	1 1/2 tsp.	7 mL
Thinly sliced fresh shiitake mushrooms	1/2 cup	125 mL
Julienned butternut squash	1/2 cup	125 mL
Soft tofu, cut into 1/2 inch (12 mm) pieces	5 oz.	140 g
White miso	2 tbsp.	30 mL

Bring water and dashi granules to a boil in a saucepan on medium. Add mushrooms and squash and simmer for 5 minutes until squash is tender-crisp.

Reduce heat to medium-low, add tofu and simmer for 2 minutes.

Remove 1/2 cup (125 mL) broth. Add miso and stir until dissolved. Slowly add miso mixture back to soup. Remove from heat (see Why To, below) and stir gently. Makes about 5 cups (1.25 L).

1 cup (250 mL): 43 Calories; 1.0 g Total Fat (0.2 g Mono, 0.6 g Poly, 0.1 g Sat); 0 mg Cholesterol; 7 g Carbohydrate; 1 g Fibre; 2 g Protein; 435 mg Sodium

ABOUT MISO
Also known as bean paste, miso is an important ingredient in Japanese cuisine. Miso is made from fermented soybeans. The consistency of miso is usually similar to peanut butter, and it is available in a variety of flavours and colours. Generally, lighter colours of miso, such as the white miso shown here, are good for more delicately flavoured dishes, while darker colours work well with bolder flavours. Miso is also highly regarded for its medicinal properties.

WHY TO
It is important not to boil the soup after the miso is added as boiling changes the flavour and, some believe, adversely alters the healthy benefits of miso.

GARNISH
thinly sliced green onion
pea sprouts

Serene sips nourish the emotions. Shiitake mushrooms and squash offer a pleasing texture to this delicate Japanese staple.

Minimalist Tempura

Broccoli florets, halved lengthwise	4	4
Fresh thin asparagus stalks, trimmed of tough ends	8	8
Peeled orange-fleshed sweet potato slices (1/4 inch, 6 mm, thick), see Tip, below	8	8
Uncooked extra-large shrimp (peeled and deveined), tails intact	8	8
Finely grated daikon radish	1/2 cup	125 mL
Finely grated ginger root	4 tsp.	20 mL
Water	1 cup	250 mL
Mirin	1/2 cup	125 mL
Tamari sauce	1/2 cup	125 mL
Instant dashi granules	2 tsp.	10 mL
Rice flour	1 cup	250 mL
Salt	1/4 tsp.	1 mL
Cold soda water	3/4 cup	175 mL
Cooking oil	3 cups	750 mL
Sesame oil	2 tbsp.	30 mL

Chill first 4 ingredients for 1 hour (see Tip, below).

Mound daikon in 4 small bowls. Top each mound with ginger and set aside.

Combine next 4 ingredients in a saucepan. Heat and stir on medium-high until boiling. Keep warm on lowest heat until ready to serve.

Whisk rice flour and salt together in a bowl. Add soda water and whisk until smooth. Batter should be the consistency of light cream.

Heat cooking and sesame oil in a large frying pan on medium-high (see Tip, page 26). Dip broccoli into batter and shallow-fry for 2 minutes until tender. Remove to a paper towel-lined plate to drain. Repeat with remaining vegetables, shallow-frying asparagus for 1 minute until tender-crisp and sweet potato for 3 minutes until tender. Dip shrimp into batter and shallow-fry for 1 minute until pink. Arrange tempura on a serving plate. Pour soy sauce mixture around daikon ginger mounds. To serve, mix some of daikon and ginger into sauce and dip tempura into mixture. Serves 4.

1 serving: 434 Calories; 11.6 g Total Fat (5.5 g Mono, 2.8 g Poly, 1.1 g Sat); 21 mg Cholesterol; 63 g Carbohydrate; 3 g Fibre; 12 g Protein; 2607 mg Sodium

TIP
Cut sweet potato pieces should be kept in water with a little lemon added to prevent discolouration.

TIP
For best results, make sure all the elements are very cold before you begin frying. Pat vegetables and shrimp dry before dipping in batter to ensure it adheres evenly during cooking. Fry just a few pieces at a time and serve immediately after cooking.

Natural elements are enhanced. Fresh shrimp and vegetables are frosted with a light, crisp tempura coating and paired with a subtle dipping sauce.

Daikon and Kabocha
With Dashi Broth

Daikon radish slices (1 1/2 inches, 3.8 cm, thick) see How To, page 213	6	6
Water	4 cups	1 L
Light soy sauce	1/4 cup	60 mL
Granulated sugar	2 tsp.	10 mL
Instant dashi granules	1 tsp.	5 mL
Piece of ginger root (1/4 inch, 6 mm, length)	1	1
Small kabocha squash, cut into 1 x 2 inch (2.5 x 5 cm) pieces (see How To, page 213)	1	1

Put daikon into a small saucepan and cover with water. Bring to a boil, reduce heat to medium and gently boil for 50 minutes until translucent. Drain.

Bring next 5 ingredients to a boil in a large frying pan. Reduce heat to medium, add daikon and simmer, uncovered, for 10 minutes.

Add squash and simmer for 10 minutes. Turn squash and daikon over and simmer for another 10 minutes until broth is reduced by half and squash is tender. Transfer daikon and squash to 6 bowls. Strain broth and discard solids. Pour a little broth into each bowl. Serves 6.

1 serving: 9 Calories; trace Total Fat (0 g Mono, trace Poly, trace Sat); 0 mg Cholesterol; 2 g Carbohydrate; trace Fibre; trace Protein; 737 mg Sodium

ABOUT KABOCHA (kah-BOH-cha) SQUASH
Kabocha looks like a green pumpkin and is known in some parts of the world as Japanese pumpkin. Look for those that have a firm, unblemished rind and that are heavy in relation to their size.

ABOUT JAPANESE FOOD PREPARATION
Presentation is as important as taste. The preparation of the vegetables into aesthetically pleasing shapes is always carefully considered. Vegetables are cut symmetrically, or with gently rounded edges. Colour is a vital consideration in the selection of ingredients and presentation.

GARNISH
shredded nori sheet

Daikon and squash pair to create a playfully beautiful dish. The intriguing appearance arouses curiosity, while the temperate flavours pamper the palate.

Roasted Asparagus
With Lemon Wasabi Cream

Fresh asparagus, trimmed of tough ends	1 lb.	454 g
Sesame oil	1 tbsp.	15 mL
Salt	1/4 tsp.	1 mL
Lemon juice	1 tbsp.	15 mL
Wasabi paste	1 tsp.	5 mL
Mayonnaise	1/4 cup	60 mL
Pepper, sprinkle		

Toss asparagus with sesame oil and salt. Arrange on a greased large baking sheet and cook in a 400°F (205°C) oven for 15 minutes until tender-crisp. Arrange on a serving plate.

Stir lemon juice and wasabi until smooth. Stir in mayonnaise and drizzle over asparagus. Sprinkle with pepper. Serves 4.

1 serving: 156 Calories; 14.6 g Total Fat (trace Mono, 0.1 g Poly, 2.0 g Sat); 5 mg Cholesterol; 5 g Carbohydrate; 2 g Fibre; 3 g Protein; 263 mg Sodium

ABOUT JAPANESE MAYONNAISE
Commercial mayonnaise was first introduced to Japan in 1925. The condiment has become a favourite complement to many dishes, both in cooking and as a side. In fact, there is one restaurant in Tokyo devoted to dishes that feature this favourite of "mayolers." Japan's per capita mayo consumption is 1.65 kg per year. Though there are variations, Japanese mayonnaise is usually made with rice vinegar and is known for its distinctly tangy taste.

Caramelized roasted asparagus is simple yet delectable. The dish is perfected with a drizzle of rich sauce, bright with citrus freshness and wasabi's distinctive bite.

Citrus Soy-Glazed Salmon

Fresh pink grapefruit juice	1 cup	250 mL
Sake	1/2 cup	125 mL
Granulated sugar	1/4 cup	60 mL
Soy sauce	1/4 cup	60 mL
Dried crushed chilies	1/4 tsp.	1 mL
Cornstarch	2 tsp.	10 mL
Water	2 tbsp.	30 mL
Mirin	2 tbsp.	30 mL
Lime juice	1 tbsp.	15 mL
Salmon fillets (4 – 5 oz., 113 – 140 g, each)	4	4
Grated lemon zest	1 tsp.	5 mL

Bring first 5 ingredients to a boil in a small saucepan on medium-high, stirring often. Boil, uncovered, for 8 minutes, stirring occasionally, until reduced by half.

Stir cornstarch and water until smooth and add to pan. Heat and stir for 10 minutes until thickened.

Stir in mirin and lime juice. Transfer 1/4 cup (60 mL) glaze to a small cup.

Cook fillets on a greased grill on medium-high for 2 to 3 minutes per side, brushing with glaze in pan, until fish flakes easily when tested with a fork. Transfer to a serving plate.

Drizzle with reserved glaze and sprinkle with lemon zest. Makes 4 fillets.

1 fillet: 353 Calories; 11.9 g Total Fat (5.0 g Mono, 3.2 g Poly, 3.5 g Sat); 57 mg Cholesterol; 27 g Carbohydrate; trace Fibre; 25 g Protein; 1371 mg Sodium

GARNISH
lemon wedges

ABOUT SODIUM IN ASIAN CUISINE
Asian dishes can often be salty. If you're watching your sodium intake, use reduced-sodium products in your cooking.

MAKE AHEAD
Glaze can be prepared one day in advance and stored in the refrigerator.

Destined to please the most refined of palates, sublime salmon is dressed to impress. A squeeze of fresh lemon further enhances the fabulous flavours.

Chicken and Seafood Hotpot

Boneless, skinless chicken thighs, cut into 1 inch (2.5 cm) pieces	1 lb.	454 g
Japanese seven-spice blend	1 tsp.	5 mL
Cooking oil	2 tsp.	10 mL
Sesame oil	2 tsp.	10 mL
Sliced carrot	1 cup	250 mL
Small Chinese dried mushrooms, rehydrated (see Tip, below)	12	12
Water	2 cups	500 mL
Mirin	1/4 cup	60 mL
Tamari sauce	1/4 cup	60 mL
Granulated sugar	1 tbsp.	15 mL
Instant dashi granules	1 tsp.	5 mL
Can of shoestring-style bamboo shoots, drained	8 oz.	227 g
Snow peas, trimmed	6 oz.	170 g
Uncooked medium shrimp (peeled and deveined)	6 oz.	170 g

Combine chicken and spice blend. Heat a wok or large frying pan on medium-high. Add cooking and sesame oil. Add chicken mixture and stir-fry for 3 minutes until browned. Transfer to a bowl.

Add carrot and mushrooms to wok and stir-fry for 3 minutes until carrot starts to soften.

Add next 5 ingredients and bring to a boil. Reduce heat to medium-low and simmer, uncovered, for 10 minutes. Add chicken and simmer for 5 minutes.

Add remaining 3 ingredients and cook for 5 minutes until shrimp turn pink. Makes about 6 cups (1.5 L).

1 cup (250 mL): 250 Calories; 9.6 g Total Fat (3.2 g Mono, 2.0 g Poly, 2.1 g Sat); 93 mg Cholesterol; 17 g Carbohydrate; 3 g Fibre; 23 g Protein; 911 mg Sodium

ABOUT DASHI (DA-shee) GRANULES
Also known as *dashi-no-moto*, dashi granules are comprised of dried tuna flakes and *kombu* (dark seaweed). Dashi granules are often used to make soup stock for staples of Japanese cuisine, such as miso soup.

TIP
To rehydrate mushrooms, put them into a bowl and cover with boiling water. Let stand, covered, for 30 minutes. Drain and squeeze dry. Remove and discard stems.

Tuck into a bowl of revamped *umani* hotpot.
Savour tender chicken, vibrant vegetables
and earthy broth—fabulously filling.

Beef Vegetable Rolls
With Miso Peanut Sauce

Hot water	1/3 cup	75 mL
Peanut butter	1/3 cup	75 mL
Mirin	2 tbsp.	30 mL
White miso	2 tbsp.	30 mL
Tamari sauce	1 tbsp.	15 mL
Garlic clove	1	1
Thin asparagus stalks (6 inches, 15 cm, long)	24	24
Enoki mushrooms, stems trimmed (see Tip, page 104)	6 oz.	170 g
Sesame oil	1 tbsp.	15 mL
Beef rouladen steaks	12	12
Japanese seven-spice blend	1 tsp.	5 mL
Cooking spray		

Process first 6 ingredients in a blender or food processor until smooth and set aside.

Toss asparagus and mushrooms with sesame oil. Arrange on a greased baking sheet and broil on top rack in oven for 5 minutes. Set aside.

Sprinkle steaks with spice blend. Arrange 2 asparagus stalks and a few mushrooms along one short edge of each steak. Roll up and secure with wooden picks. Arrange on a greased wire rack set in a baking sheet and spray rolls with cooking spray. Broil on top rack in oven for 3 minutes per side until browned. Remove to a serving plate and drizzle with sauce. Makes 12 rolls.

1 roll: 184 Calories; 11.0 g Total Fat (2.4 g Mono, 0.3 g Poly, 3.1 g Sat); 34 mg Cholesterol; 6 g Carbohydrate; 2 g Fibre; 15 g Protein; 223 mg Sodium

---

SERVING SUGGESTION
The most common Japanese meal follows the form of *ichiju-sansai*, or "soup plus three." In terms of the table setting, rice is served on the left, miso soup on the right and three "side dishes" (seen as complements to the rice) appear in the centre and behind. Each of the three accessory dishes employs a different cooking technique—pickling, broiling and simmering, for example. Each person at the table receives individual servings of each.

Guests won't be able to resist the **visually tempting** contrast of thinly sliced **melt-in-your-mouth** beef wrapped around vibrant **asparagus**. Taste the **peanut-infused** drizzle with every bite.

Plum Sake Sorbet

Red and black plums, pitted and chopped	1 1/2 lbs.	680 g
Water	1/4 cup	60 mL
Mirin	2 tbsp.	30 mL
Sake	2 tbsp.	30 mL
Water	3/4 cup	175 mL
Granulated sugar	1/2 cup	125 mL

Bring plums and water to a boil in a saucepan. Reduce heat to medium. Cook, covered, for 5 minutes, stirring occasionally, until plums are soft. Transfer to a blender or food processor.

Add mirin and sake.

Heat and stir water and sugar in a saucepan on medium until sugar is dissolved. Add to plum mixture and carefully process until almost smooth (see Safety Tip, below). Pour into a 2 quart (2 L) dish and freeze, covered, for 4 hours until almost firm. Stir to break up ice crystals and process until smooth. Freeze until firm. Makes about 4 cups (1 L).

1/2 cup (125 mL): 101 Calories; 0.2 g Total Fat (0.1 g Mono, trace Poly, trace Sat); 0 mg Cholesterol; 24 g Carbohydrate; 1 g Fibre; 1 g Protein; trace Sodium

GARNISH
plum slices

SAFETY TIP
Follow manufacturer's instructions for blending hot liquids.

MAKE AHEAD
The sorbet can be made up to one month in advance. It may need to stand for five minutes at room temperature to soften before scooping.

Blushing sorbet fortified with sake is a double-agent—posing as a refreshing palate cleanser between courses, and satiating that craving for sweetness as the meal draws to a close.

Korean dishes are traditionally served as sides to accompany the ubiquitous rice—perfect for relaxed, buffet-style meals with friends. Encourage guests to dish up from a spread of steaming rice and fiery Korean specialties. Offer ramekins of spicy kimchee and sleek metal chopsticks, unique to Korean cuisine. Set the scene for lively conversation and spontaneous energy—cloak your table in white for luck, hanging rice paper parasols for an infusion of colour.

Korean

Spice With Substance

Kimchee Crab Cakes

Can of frozen crabmeat, thawed, cartilage removed, squeezed dry (see Tip, below)	11.3 oz.	320 g
Finely chopped cabbage kimchee, drained	1/2 cup	125 mL
Chopped green onion	3 tbsp.	50 mL
Pepper	1/4 tsp.	1 mL
White bread slices, torn into pieces	2	2
Large egg	1	1
Mirin	2 tbsp.	30 mL
Korean hot pepper paste	2 tsp.	10 mL
Cooking oil	2 tbsp.	30 mL

Combine first 4 ingredients in a bowl.

Process bread in a blender or food processor until fine crumbs and add to crab mixture.

Process next 3 ingredients until smooth. Add to bowl and mix well. Shape into patties, about 1 inch (2.5 cm) in diameter, using about 1 tbsp. (15 mL) for each.

Heat 1 tbsp. (15 mL) cooking oil in a large frying pan on medium. Cook crab cakes in 2 batches for 3 minutes per side until browned. Makes about 30 crab cakes.

1 crab cake: 49 Calories; 1.3 g Total Fat (0.6 g Mono, 0.3 g Poly, 0.2 g Sat); 17 mg Cholesterol; 6 g Carbohydrate; trace Fibre; 3 g Protein; 396 mg Sodium

ABOUT CABBAGE KIMCHEE
Made from fermented cabbage, this fiery condiment is a staple in Korean kitchens and provides a quick way to give an aromatic flare to your meal. Assorted varieties of vegetables may be used to create other types of kimchee.

TIP
Frozen canned crabmeat is a product truer to fresh than the regular canned variety.

MAKE AHEAD
Make and refrigerate crab cakes up to one day in advance. Reheat in 375°F (190°C) oven for 10 minutes until hot.

Fanciful fusion. This adaptation of *jun*, or **flatcakes**, merges the **western** crabcake with Korean flavours. One bite confirms a **perfect match**.

Fiery Vegetable Bites

Water	3/4 cup	175 mL
Short-grain white rice, rinsed and drained	1/2 cup	125 mL
Mirin	1 tbsp.	15 mL
Rice vinegar	1 tbsp.	15 mL
Granulated sugar	2 tsp.	10 mL
Salt	1/8 tsp.	0.5 mL
Sesame oil	2 tsp.	10 mL
Finely chopped fresh shiitake mushrooms	1/2 cup	125 mL
Finely diced orange pepper	1/2 cup	125 mL
Finely diced zucchini	1/2 cup	125 mL
Finely chopped chives	2 tbsp.	30 mL
Finely chopped small red chili pepper (see Tip, page 148)	1 tbsp.	15 mL
Garlic cloves, minced	2	2
Salt	1/2 tsp.	2 mL
Nori sheet, finely chopped	1/2	1/2

Bring water and rice to a boil in a small saucepan. Reduce heat to medium-low and simmer, covered, for 12 minutes, without lifting the lid, until rice is tender and liquid is absorbed. Remove from heat and let stand, covered, for 10 minutes. Transfer to a bowl.

Stir next 4 ingredients until sugar is dissolved. Add to rice and stir. Let stand until cool.

Heat sesame oil in a medium frying pan on medium. Add next 7 ingredients and cook for 5 minutes, stirring occasionally, until zucchini is tender-crisp.

Add nori and vegetables to rice and mix well. With wet hands (see Why To, below), shape into 1 inch (2.5 cm) balls. Makes about 25 rice balls.

1 rice ball: 19 Calories; 0.4 g Total Fat (trace Mono, trace Poly, 0.1 g Sat); 0 mg Cholesterol; 3 g Carbohydrate; trace Fibre; trace Protein; 60 mg Sodium

ABOUT SHORT-GRAIN RICE
Short-grain rice is tender and soft when cooked, and it has a higher starch content, making it stickier than long-grain rice. This quality makes it popular in Asian cooking methods where the rice is being formed by hand, such as in sushi and these rice balls.

TIP
You can use any combination of vegetables you choose—bok choy, daikon and cucumber, for example.

WHY TO
Wetting your hands before rolling will prevent the rice from sticking to them.

Tender mouthfuls that pack a punch. These rice balls allude to Japanese cuisine, but the chili heat makes them distinctly Korean. Kick up your gathering by offering a generous number.

Bulgogi Beef

Ingredient	Imperial	Metric
Granulated sugar	1/4 cup	60 mL
Mirin	1/4 cup	60 mL
Sesame oil	1/4 cup	60 mL
Soy sauce	1/4 cup	60 mL
Chopped green onion (white part only)	2 tbsp.	30 mL
Garlic cloves, minced	4	4
Finely grated ginger root	2 tsp.	10 mL
Pepper	1/2 tsp.	2 mL
Beef rib-eye steak (1 inch, 2.5 cm, thick) thinly sliced (see Tip, page 208)	1 1/2 lbs.	680 g
Cornstarch	1 tsp.	5 mL
Cooking oil	1 tbsp.	15 mL

Combine first 8 ingredients in a large resealable freezer bag. Add beef and marinate in the refrigerator for 2 hours.

Drain marinade into a small cup. Stir in cornstarch until smooth and set aside.

Heat a wok or large frying pan on medium-high. Add cooking oil. Add beef and stir-fry for 2 minutes until browned. Transfer to a bowl and set aside. Stir reserved marinade and add to wok. Stir for 1 minute until bubbling and thickened. Return beef to wok and stir until coated. Makes about 4 cups (1 L).

1/2 cup (125 mL): 228 Calories; 13.3 g Total Fat (2.8 g Mono, 0.7 g Poly, 2.8 g Sat); 45 mg Cholesterol; 10 g Carbohydrate; trace Fibre; 15 g Protein; 688 mg Sodium

---

GARNISH
toasted sesame seeds
sliced green onion

ABOUT BULGOGI
This consummately Korean dish is recognized for its tender meat. Good-quality cuts are always used, and the meat is well-marinated. This dish is often wrapped in lettuce leaves and eaten with rice.

A **must-have** for a Korean menu. Tender,
marinated beef with a memorable **aroma**.
Succulent **flavours** flood the senses.

Four-Season Dumpling Soup

Lean ground pork	6 oz.	170 g
Bean sprouts, trimmed and chopped	1 cup	250 mL
Chopped cabbage kimchee, drained	1/2 cup	125 mL
Chinese dried mushrooms, rehydrated (see Tip, page 84), finely chopped	2	2
Sesame seeds, toasted (see Tip, page 128)	3 tbsp.	50 mL
Finely grated ginger root	2 tsp.	10 mL
Garlic cloves, minced	2	2
Salt	1/2 tsp.	2 mL
Pepper	1/4 tsp.	1 mL
Round dumpling wrappers	30	30
Prepared chicken broth	8 cups	2 L
Hoisin sauce	1/3 cup	75 mL

Combine first 9 ingredients.

Spoon about 1 tbsp. (15 mL) filling onto centre of 1 dumpling wrapper. Dampen edges with water. Fold to enclose and press edges together to seal. Stand upright on a parchment paper-lined tray and cover with greased plastic wrap to prevent drying out. Repeat steps. Makes about 30 dumplings.

Combine broth and hoisin sauce in a Dutch oven and bring to a boil on medium-high. Add dumplings to broth, 1 at a time. Cook for 5 minutes until dumplings rise to surface and are no longer pink inside. Spoon into serving bowls. Serves 8.

1 serving: 147 Calories; 5.9 g Total Fat (1.9 g Mono, 0.7 g Poly, 1.5 g Sat); 14 mg Cholesterol; 17 g Carbohydrate; 1 g Fibre; 7 g Protein; 2301 mg Sodium

GARNISH (SEE HOW TO, PAGE 213)
thin slices of daikon radish,
  cut into flowers
large red pepper,
  cut into leaf shapes
large yellow pepper,
  cut into small circles
thin slices of carrot,
  cut into stars
pea shoots

ABOUT MAKING DUMPLINGS
With kitchen parties becoming more and more popular, you may decide to go with an Asian theme and invite your guests to make the dumplings with you. Preparing Asian food can be as much fun as eating it!

Korea's cuisine is closely tied to its distinct seasons. This soup celebrates all four with beautifully cut vegetables dancing among the dumplings. Red autumn leaves, white spring blossoms, yellow summer suns and orange winter night-sky stars fill this fragrant soup.

Summer Soba Salad

Soy sauce	1/4 cup	60 mL
Rice vinegar	3 tbsp.	50 mL
Sweet chili sauce	3 tbsp.	50 mL
Liquid honey	2 tbsp.	30 mL
Mirin	2 tbsp.	30 mL
Sesame oil	2 tbsp.	30 mL
Sesame seeds, toasted (see Tip, page 128)	1 tbsp.	15 mL
Pepper	1/4 tsp.	1 mL
Soba (buckwheat noodles)	6 oz.	170 g
Shredded suey choy (green part only)	2 cups	500 mL
Julienned red pepper	3/4 cup	175 mL
Julienned yellow pepper	3/4 cup	175 mL
Julienned carrot	1/2 cup	125 mL
Julienned daikon radish	1/2 cup	125 mL
Julienned English cucumber	1/2 cup	125 mL
Julienned red cabbage	1/2 cup	125 mL
Thinly sliced green onion	1/4 cup	60 mL

Combine first 8 ingredients in a large bowl. Reserve 1/2 cup (125 mL) and set aside.

Cook noodles in a large saucepan of boiling salted water for 5 minutes until tender but firm. Rinse under cold water until cool. Drain well. Add to bowl and toss.

Spread suey choy on a large platter and place noodles in centre. Arrange next 6 ingredients over noodles and sprinkle with green onion. Drizzle with reserved dressing. Toss just before serving. Makes about 9 cups (2.25 L).

1 cup (250 mL): 149 Calories; 4.1 g Total Fat (0.2 g Mono, 0.2 g Poly, 0.5 g Sat); 0 mg Cholesterol; 25 g Carbohydrate; 2 g Fibre; 3 g Protein; 678 mg Sodium

ABOUT SOBA
These noodles are made from buckwheat and wheat flour. Popular in both Japanese street foods and more refined fare, they are also a staple in Korean cooking. The word *soba* can also refer to any thin noodle.

SERVING SUGGESTION
Serve with Kalbi, page 110, and a cold beer, chilled semi-dry white wine or slightly chilled light-bodied red wine.

MAKE AHEAD
Prepare, assemble and refrigerate up to eight hours in advance. Marinate noodles but keep separate from vegetables until ready to serve. Toss them from time to time to ensure even flavours.

A stunning rainbow of crunchy fresh vegetables with earthy buckwheat noodles in a sweet and spicy dressing.

Kochujang Chicken

Korean hot pepper paste	2 tbsp.	30 mL
Granulated sugar	1 tbsp.	15 mL
Sake	1 tbsp.	15 mL
Soy sauce	1 tbsp.	15 mL
Garlic cloves, minced	2	2
Finely grated ginger root	1 tsp.	5 mL
Boneless, skinless chicken thighs, thinly sliced (see Tip, page 208)	1 lb.	454 g
Sesame oil	1 tbsp.	15 mL
Sliced fresh shiitake mushrooms	3 cups	750 mL
Thinly sliced green pepper	1 cup	250 mL
Thinly sliced onion	1 cup	250 mL
Julienned carrot	1/2 cup	125 mL
Thinly sliced cabbage kimchee	1/2 cup	125 mL
Finely chopped small red chili peppers (see Tip, page 148)	1 tbsp.	15 mL

Combine first 6 ingredients in a bowl. Add chicken, stir and marinate in the refrigerator, covered, for 30 minutes. Drain and discard marinade.

Heat a wok or large frying pan on medium-high. Add sesame oil. Add chicken and stir-fry for 1 minute.

Add remaining 6 ingredients and stir-fry for 5 minutes until onion and mushrooms are softened. Makes about 6 cups (1.5 L).

1 cup (250 mL): 245 Calories; 8.5 g Total Fat (2.2 g Mono, 1.3 g Poly, 1.9 g Sat); 50 mg Cholesterol; 24 g Carbohydrate; 6 g Fibre; 17 g Protein; 813 mg Sodium

---

ABOUT KOREAN MENUS
Rice is always the centrepiece in a Korean meal, as is, most often, kimchee. These staples are accompanied by a selection of several *banchan*, or "side dishes," which may or may not have meat. Recipes are characterized by pungent, robust flavours and heat that can have the palate buzzing. However, not all Korean dishes are spicy. The meal is designed to create a balance of flavours.

Exotic and earthy scents entice. Don't be
surprised if your guests make the Korean pronouncement,
jalmukesumneda (I will eat well),
when they come to your table.

Kimchee Beef Stew

Cooking oil	2 tsp.	10 mL
Beef top sirloin steak, thinly sliced (see Tip, page 208)	1/2 lb.	225 g
Sliced cabbage kimchee	1 1/2 cups	375 mL
Thinly sliced onion	1 cup	250 mL
Diced red pepper	1/4 cup	60 mL
Garlic cloves, minced	2	2
Prepared beef broth	3 cups	750 mL
Korean hot pepper paste	1 tbsp.	15 mL
Soy sauce	1 tbsp.	15 mL
Granulated sugar	2 tsp.	10 mL
Sliced fresh shiitake mushrooms	1/2 cup	125 g
Enoki mushrooms, stems trimmed (see Tip, below)	2 1/2 oz.	70 g
Thinly sliced leek (white part only)	1/4 cup	60 mL
Small red chili pepper, sliced (see Tip, page 148)	1	1

Heat cooking oil in a large saucepan on medium-high. Add beef and stir-fry for 1 minute until no longer pink.

Add next 4 ingredients and stir-fry for 2 minutes until onion is softened.

Add next 4 ingredients and bring to a boil.

Stir in remaining 4 ingredients. Reduce heat to medium and simmer, uncovered, for 2 minutes to blend flavours. Makes about 6 cups (1.5 L).

1 cup (250 mL): 138 Calories; 4.7 g Total Fat (2.1 g Mono, 0.6 g Poly, 1.3 g Sat); 20 mg Cholesterol; 13 g Carbohydrate; 2 g Fibre; 11 g Protein; 2184 mg Sodium

ABOUT ENOKI (en-OH-kee) MUSHROOMS
These long-stemmed mushrooms are topped by an umbrella-like cap and can be found in both Asian and Western markets. Desired for their crisp texture, enoki are best eaten when lightly cooked. Select enoki mushrooms that are firm and unblemished.

TIP
To trim enoki mushrooms, cut about an inch (2.5 cm) off the bottom of the stem and leave the rest intact.

Inviting **warmth** and **comfort** in one dish.
Served with **rice**, this makes a satisfying meal.

Tofu Vegetable Stew

Cooking oil	1 tbsp.	15 mL
Finely grated ginger root	1 tbsp.	15 mL
Garlic cloves, minced	3	3
Korean hot pepper paste	1 tbsp.	15 mL
Sesame oil	1 tbsp.	15 mL
Soy sauce	1 tbsp.	15 mL
Medium tofu, cut into 1/2 inch (12 mm) cubes	10 oz.	285 g
Prepared vegetable broth	1 1/2 cups	375 mL
Mirin	1/4 cup	60 mL
Chopped zucchini (1 inch, 2.5 cm, pieces)	2 cups	500 mL
Chopped green pepper	1 cup	250 mL
Chopped yellow pepper	1 cup	250 mL
Sliced celery	1 cup	250 mL
Thinly sliced small red chili peppers (see Tip, page 148)	2	2
Thinly sliced green onion	2 tbsp.	30 mL

Heat cooking oil in a large saucepan on medium-high. Add next 5 ingredients and stir for 1 minute. Add tofu and cook for 3 minutes, stirring occasionally.

Add broth and mirin and bring to a boil.

Add next 5 ingredients and stir. Reduce heat to medium-low and simmer, covered, for 15 minutes until vegetables are tender-crisp. Transfer to a serving bowl.

Sprinkle with green onion. Makes about 6 cups (1.5 L).

1 cup (250 mL): 133 Calories; 6.4 g Total Fat (1.6 g Mono, 1.5 g Poly, 0.7 g Sat); 0 mg Cholesterol; 14 g Carbohydrate; 2 g Fibre; 4 g Protein; 429 mg Sodium

PRESENTATION INSPIRATION
For an authentic presentation, serve the stew with metal chopsticks, which are more typical than their bamboo counterparts. But don't banish the spoon. Because of the many soups and stews in Korean cooking, spoons are also an authentic—and handy—utensil.

GARNISH
small red chili peppers

Korean **nostalgia**, modern favourite. Follow your whim and **vary the heat** to your taste by reducing or increasing the **pepper paste** and **fresh chillies**.

Bibimbap

(Rice, Beef and Vegetable Bowl)

Korean hot pepper paste	1/4 cup	60 mL
Brown sugar, packed	2 tbsp.	30 mL
Sesame oil	2 tbsp.	30 mL
Soy sauce	1 tbsp.	15 mL
Garlic cloves, minced	2	2
Cooking oil	1 tbsp.	15 mL
Sesame oil	1 tbsp.	15 mL
Cooked long-grain rice (about 1 1/3 cup, 325 mL, uncooked)	4 cups	1 L
Cooking oil	1/2 tsp.	2 mL
Beef rib-eye steak, thinly sliced (see Tip, page 208)	1/2 lb.	225 g
Korean barbecue sauce	3 tbsp.	50 mL
Sesame seeds, toasted (see Tip, page 128)	1 tbsp.	15 mL
Cooking oil	1/2 tsp.	2 mL
Enoki mushrooms, stems trimmed (see Tip, page 104)	3 1/2 oz.	100 g
Mirin	2 tbsp.	30 mL
Fresh spinach leaves, lightly packed, blanched and squeezed dry	3 cups	750 mL
Julienned carrot	1/2 cup	125 mL
Julienned radish	1/2 cup	125 mL
Onion sprouts	1/2 cup	125 mL
Cooking oil	1/2 tsp.	2 mL
Large eggs	2	2

Combine first 5 ingredients in a small bowl and set aside. Makes about 1/2 cup (125 mL).

Heat a cast iron pan on medium. Grease with cooking and sesame oil. Spread rice in bottom and up sides of pan and heat for 20 minutes until bottom is golden and crust has formed. Reduce heat to low.

Heat a wok or large frying pan on medium-high and add cooking oil. Add next 3 ingredients and stir-fry for 3 minutes until browned. Arrange in a wedge over the rice.

Wipe wok clean and heat cooking oil on medium-high. Add mushrooms and mirin and stir-fry for 1 minute until softened. Arrange in a smaller wedge next to meat mixture.

Arrange next 4 ingredients in wedges over remaining rice.

Heat cooking oil in wok on medium-low. Break eggs into pan and cook for 5 minutes until white is just set. Place in centre of dish. Toss in pan before serving. Serve with pepper sauce. Serves 4.

1 serving: 1152 Calories; 24.6 g Total Fat (4.7 g Mono, 2.4 g Poly, 4.3 g Sat); 138 mg Cholesterol; 193 g Carbohydrate; 8 g Fibre; 36 g Protein; 1381 mg Sodium

In a restaurant, this dish might arrive to the table in a sizzling hot stone bowl. A golden-crisp crust on the bottom of the rice is the foundation of this attractive meal-in-one.

Kalbi

(Barbecued Beef Short Ribs)

Brown sugar, packed	1/2 cup	125 mL
Mirin	1/2 cup	125 mL
Soy sauce	1/2 cup	125 mL
Kiwifruit	1	1
Rice vinegar	1/4 cup	60 mL
Finely grated ginger root	2 tbsp.	30 mL
Garlic cloves, minced	6	6
Sesame oil	2 tbsp.	30 mL
Pepper	1 tsp.	5 mL
Korean-style beef short ribs	3 lbs.	1.4 kg

Process first 9 ingredients in a blender or food processor until smooth. Reserve 1/2 cup (125 mL) marinade and chill.

Pour remaining marinade into a large resealable freezer bag. Add ribs and marinate in the refrigerator for 4 hours (see Tip, below). Drain and discard marinade. Cook ribs on a greased grill on medium-high, brushing with reserved marinade, for 4 minutes per side until well done. Serves 4.

1 serving: 1048 Calories; 76.2 g Total Fat (31.0 g Mono, 2.6 g Poly, 30.3 g Sat); 154 mg Cholesterol; 45 g Carbohydrate; 1 g Fibre; 39 g Protein; 2726 mg Sodium

ABOUT KOREAN-STYLE BEEF SHORT RIBS
Beef short ribs are a thick and fatty cut of beef that requires lengthy, slow cooking. When cut Korean-style, the ribs are cut crosswise into thin strips, making them a quick and convenient ingredient in Asian cooking.

TIP
The acidic quality of kiwifruit works well to tenderize meat and its subtle sweetness won't overpower the other flavours. Be careful not to marinate for too long as the texture of the meat will break down.

SERVING SUGGESTION
Try this dish with Summer Soba Salad, page 100, and a cold beer or a chilled semi-dry white or light-bodied red wine.

GARNISH
sliced green onion
toasted sesame seeds

Korean **barbecue** is justifiably **famous**.
The sweet, gingery kiwi marinade
imbues these short ribs with delicious
flavour and remarkable **tenderness**.

Cinnamon Fruit "Cocktail"

Red grapes	18	18
Green grapes	18	18
Skewers (4 inches, 10 cm, each)	12	12
Liquid honey	1/2 cup	125 mL
Water	1/4 cup	60 mL
Cinnamon sticks (4 inches, 10 cm, each)	2	2
Piece of ginger root (3 inch, 7.5 cm, length) quartered	1	1
Goldschlager liqueur	3/4 cup	175 mL

Thread grapes, alternating colours, onto skewers. Freeze in an airtight container.

Combine next 4 ingredients in a saucepan and bring to a boil. Reduce heat to medium-low and simmer for 15 minutes to blend flavours. Discard cinnamon sticks and ginger. Transfer syrup to a liquid measure and chill.

Pour syrup into 6 chilled martini glasses. Carefully pour 1 oz. (30 mL) liqueur into each glass. Put 2 skewers into each glass. Serves 6.

1 serving: 212 Calories; 0.1 g Total Fat (trace Mono, 0.1 g Poly, trace Sat); 0 mg Cholesterol; 41 g Carbohydrate; trace Fibre; trace Protein; 2 mg Sodium

ABOUT MEDICINAL PROPERTIES OF SPICES
In Korean cooking, as in several other Asian cuisines, the medicinal properties of foods are very important. Both cinnamon and ginger are thought to aid digestion.

MAKE AHEAD
Make and refrigerate syrup up to one day in advance. Thread the grapes onto skewers and freeze in an airtight container up to two days in advance.

A glamourous finish to cool the kimchee fire.
In this refreshing and elegant cocktail, frozen grapes
adorn a lightly cinnamon- and ginger-infused
nip of Goldschlager.

For centuries, Lebanon has absorbed the diverse culinary influences of Mediterranean, Middle Eastern and European cultures. It is a small country with big flavour. Fitting then, that Lebanon's cuisine is renowned for lush assortments of *mezze*, small bites with big impact that are synonymous with people gathering around lovingly-prepared plates, eagerly sharing food and good company. Offer guests a spread of authentic appetizers on a sunflower-yellow tablecloth, contrasting with azure plates.

Lebanese

Cultural Mosaic

Smoky Seven-Spice Hummus

Can of chickpeas, rinsed and drained	19 oz.	540 mL
Extra virgin olive oil	1/3 cup	75 mL
Lemon juice	2 tbsp.	30 mL
Tahini	2 tbsp.	30 mL
Lebanese seven-spice blend	1 tbsp.	15 mL
Garlic clove, minced	1	1
Liquid honey	1 tsp.	5 mL
Smoked sweet paprika	1/2 tsp.	2 mL
Salt	1/4 tsp.	1 mL

Process all 9 ingredients in a blender or food processor until smooth and transfer to a serving bowl. Makes about 2 cups (500 mL).

1/2 cup (125 mL): 328 Calories; 24.7 g Total Fat (15.3 g Mono, 5.5 g Poly, 3.2 g Sat); 0 mg Cholesterol; 23 g Carbohydrate; 6 g Fibre; 8 g Protein; 293 mg Sodium

---

GARNISH
drizzle of extra virgin olive oil
cinnamon stick
peppercorns
cardamom pods

Quick and easy preparation allows for more time with guests. The rich, yet light, texture of hummus provides the perfect foil for classic Lebanese spices and a sweet and smoky twist. Serve with torn pita bread or pita chips.

Classic Tabbouleh

Bulgur, fine grind	1/2 cup	125 mL
Finely chopped fresh parsley (see Tip, below)	2 1/2 cups	625 mL
Diced seeded tomato	1 cup	250 mL
Finely chopped fresh mint	1/2 cup	125 mL
Finely chopped green onion	1/2 cup	125 mL
Lemon juice	1/3 cup	75 mL
Extra virgin olive oil	2 tbsp.	30 mL
Salt	3/4 tsp.	4 mL
Pepper	1/4 tsp.	1 mL

Cover bulgur with boiling water. Stir and let stand for 20 minutes until tender. Drain well and transfer to a large bowl.

Add next 4 ingredients and toss.

Combine remaining 4 ingredients, drizzle over parsley mixture and toss. Makes about 5 cups (1.25 L).

1/2 cup (125 mL): 61 Calories; 3.0 g Total Fat (2.1 g Mono, 0.5 g Poly, 0.4 g Sat); 0 mg Cholesterol; 8 g Carbohydrate; 2 g Fibre; 2 g Protein; 250 mg Sodium

ABOUT BULGUR
Sometimes known as bulgur wheat or *burghul*, this nutritious grain is widely used in Middle Eastern cooking and is similar to cracked wheat. Bulgur comes from wheat kernels that have been steamed, dried and crushed and is available in coarse, medium and fine grinds.

TIP
Use a salad spinner to dry the parsley and mint. With a sharp knife, finely slice the herbs rather than chopping them in the food processor, which can crush them and make them mushy.

ABOUT TABBOULEH (tuh-BOO-luh)
Tabbouleh is a classic Lebanese dish. While North Americanized tabbouleh sometimes features more bulgur than parsley, those passionate about making it authentically use lots of parsley and no cucumber. In Lebanon, tabbouleh is traditionally eaten scooped up in a crisp romaine leaf rather than with a fork.

MAKE AHEAD
Prepare and combine the bulgur and herbs; chop and combine the green onions and tomato; refrigerate. Combine all ingredients 30 minutes to one hour before serving and mix in the dressing just before serving.

Discover for yourself why this seemingly simple salad has been elevated to the status of a national dish of Lebanon. Nourishing bulgur is given freshness and a refreshing edge when tumbled with fresh herbs, olive oil and lemon.

Za'atar Stuffed Grape Leaves

Long-grain white rice	1/2 cup	125 mL
Lean ground lamb	6 oz.	170 g
Za'atar spice blend (see Tip, below)	2 tsp.	10 mL
Salt	1 tsp.	5 mL
Grape leaves, rinsed and drained, tough stems removed	16	16
Water	1 cup	250 mL
Lemon juice	3 tbsp.	50 mL
Plain yogurt	1 cup	250 mL
Chopped fresh mint	2 tbsp.	30 mL

Put rice into a bowl, cover with boiling water and let stand for 15 minutes (see Why To, below). Drain and rinse with cold water.

Combine rice with next 3 ingredients.

Spoon about 1 tbsp. (15 mL) lamb mixture onto vein side of each leaf. Fold and roll to enclose filling (see How To, page 214). Arrange, seam-side down, in a large saucepan.

Pour water over stuffed leaves and bring to a boil. Reduce heat to medium-low and simmer, covered, for 15 minutes.

Add lemon juice and simmer for another 15 minutes until internal temperature reaches 175°F (80°C). Remove from heat and let stand, covered, for 20 minutes. Arrange on a serving plate.

Combine yogurt and mint and serve with stuffed grape leaves. Makes 16 grape leaves.

1 grape leaf with 1 tbsp. (15 mL) yogurt mixture: 54 Calories; 1.5 g Total Fat (0.6 g Mono, 0.2 g Poly, 0.6 g Sat); 7 mg Cholesterol; 7 g Carbohydrate; trace Fibre; 3 g Protein; 162 mg Sodium

---

GARNISH
sprigs of mint
strips of lemon peel

TIP
If you are looking for ways to use up the za'atar spice blend, try some of these quick ideas:
- Za'atar Pita: Brush pita bread with olive oil. Sprinkle lightly with za'atar. Bake or broil until toasted.
- Za'atar Fried Eggs: Heat enough olive oil to coat the bottom of a non-stick frying pan on medium. Cover bottom of pan with a thin layer of za'atar. Break eggs onto za'atar. Cook until they reach desired doneness. Serve with toasted pita.

WHY TO
Soaking the rice in boiling water first will help it absorb water more readily when being cooked, allowing it to cook more evenly.

Grapes have always been associated with abundance—maybe that's why these leaf-wrapped morsels of lamb and rice seem so decadent. Revel in their divinely tangy flavours.

Fattoush

Whole-wheat pita bread (7 inch, 18 cm, diameter)	1	1
Extra virgin olive oil	1 tsp.	5 mL
Za'atar spice blend (see Tip, page 120)	2 tsp.	10 mL
Shredded Romaine lettuce, lightly packed	4 cups	1 L
Diced Lebanese cucumber	1 cup	250 mL
Diced seeded Roma (plum) tomato	1 cup	250 mL
Sliced radish	1/2 cup	125 mL
Chopped fresh mint (see How To, below)	1/3 cup	75 mL
Chopped fresh parsley (see How To, below)	1/3 cup	75 mL
Diced green pepper	1/3 cup	75 mL
Thinly sliced red onion (1 inch, 2.5 cm, pieces)	1/3 cup	75 mL
Extra virgin olive oil	1/3 cup	75 mL
Lemon juice	1/3 cup	75 mL
Grated lemon zest	1/2 tsp.	2 mL
Garlic clove, minced	1	1
Salt	1 tsp.	5 mL
Pepper	1/4 tsp.	1 mL

Brush both sides of pita with olive oil and sprinkle with za'atar. Bake directly on centre rack in a 325°F (160°C) oven for 10 minutes per side until crisp and dry. Cool on a wire rack. Break into 1 inch (2.5 cm) pieces and put into a bowl.

Add next 8 ingredients.

Combine remaining 6 ingredients, drizzle over salad and toss. Makes about 8 cups (2 L) salad.

1 cup (250 mL): 127 Calories; 10.3 g Total Fat (7.1 g Mono, 1.6 g Poly, 1.5 g Sat); 0 mg Cholesterol; 9 g Carbohydrate; 2 g Fibre; 2 g Protein; 342 mg Sodium

---

ABOUT LEBANESE CUCUMBERS
Lebanese cucumbers are like miniature English cucumbers. They're small (usually no longer than 5 to 6 inches, 12 to 15 cm), almost seedless, sweet and juicy and are eaten with the deep green peel left on. Unpeeled English cucumbers can be used in their place.

HOW TO CHOP HERBS
Use a very sharp knife or scissors to chop mint and parsley so the leaves are cleanly cut, not bruised. Mint is especially susceptible to blackened edges if not cut cleanly.

MAKE AHEAD
Put the vegetables and herbs into the bottom of the bowl with the lettuce lightly set on top, cover with plastic wrap and refrigerate for up to four hours. Toss with the dressing and pita. Prepare and refrigerate dressing up to two days in advance, but bring to room temperature before combining with the salad ingredients because the olive oil will solidify a bit in the fridge.

This **fresh-tasting** salad is a celebration of **bright, tangy** flavours and **crisp** and **crunchy** textures. Buy the freshest and tastiest **vegetables** and **herbs** at the market, and the preparation will be a **joyful** experience right to the final tossing.

Fatayer Bi Sabanikh
(Spinach Pies)

Olive oil	1 tsp.	5 mL
Chopped onion	2/3 cup	150 mL
Box of frozen chopped spinach, thawed and squeezed dry (see Tip, below)	10 oz.	300 g
Chopped parsley	1/4 cup	60 mL
Lemon juice	1/4 cup	60 mL
Olive oil	2 tbsp.	30 mL
Sumac	1/2 tsp.	2 mL
Salt	1/2 tsp.	2 mL
Pepper	1/4 tsp.	1 mL
Ground allspice	1/8 tsp.	0.5 mL
Ground cinnamon	1/8 tsp.	0.5 mL
Frozen dinner roll dough, covered, thawed in refrigerator overnight	12	12

Heat olive oil in a frying pan on medium. Add onion and cook for 8 minutes until softened. Transfer to a bowl.

Add next 9 ingredients. Stir well.

Roll out each dough portion on a lightly floured surface to a 4 inch (10 cm) round. Spoon about 1 1/2 tbsp. (25 mL) filling onto centre of each round (see How To, page 214). Dampen edges of dough with water. Fold edges toward centre in 3 sections, forming a triangle. Press edges firmly to seal. Arrange on a greased baking sheet and cover with greased plastic wrap. Let stand in oven with light on and door closed for 30 minutes until doubled in size. Bake in a 400°F (205°C) oven for 15 minutes until golden brown. Makes 12 fatayer.

1 fatayer: 130 Calories; 4.8 g Total Fat (2.0 g Mono, 0.4 g Poly, 0.4 g Sat); 0 mg Cholesterol; 19 g Carbohydrate; 1 g Fibre; 4 g Protein; 260 mg Sodium

TIP
You can use either fresh or frozen spinach for this dish, depending on what you have on hand. If using fresh, blanch spinach and squeeze dry.

ABOUT FATAYER BI SABANIKH
This dish is traditionally eaten during Lent, a time when the faithful abstain from eating meat.

In Lebanon, a party isn't a party without a tray of these **tender spinach pastries**. Golden bread dough enfolds a filling that **sparkles** with the **zesty** freshness characteristic of **Lebanese** cooking.

Yogurt Chickpea Stew

Butter	1 tbsp.	15 mL
Finely chopped onion	1 cup	250 mL
Garlic cloves, minced	3	3
Salt	1/2 tsp.	2 mL
Tomato paste	3 tbsp.	50 mL
Can of diced tomatoes (with liquid)	19 oz.	540 mL
Can of chickpeas (garbanzo beans), rinsed and drained	19 oz.	540 mL
Cinnamon sticks (4 inches, 10 cm, each)	2	2
Balkan-style yogurt	1 cup	250 mL
Chopped fresh mint	1/4 cup	60 mL
Garlic clove, minced	1	1
Finely chopped red onion	1 tbsp.	15 mL
Pine nuts, toasted (see Tip, page 128)	1 tbsp.	15 mL
Finely chopped fresh parsley	1 tsp.	5 mL

Melt butter in a frying pan on medium. Add next 3 ingredients and cook for 10 minutes until onion is browned.

Add tomato paste and stir for 1 minute.

Add next 3 ingredients and bring to a boil. Reduce heat to medium-low and simmer for 10 minutes until mixture is slightly reduced. Discard cinnamon sticks and transfer to a serving bowl.

Combine next 3 ingredients and spoon some of mixture onto stew.

Sprinkle chickpea mixture with remaining 3 ingredients and serve with remaining yogurt mixture. Makes about 4 cups (1L).

1/2 cup (125 mL): 122 Calories; 3.2 g Total Fat (0.8 g Mono, 1.0 g Poly, 1.0 g Sat); 5 mg Cholesterol; 19 g Carbohydrate; 3 g Fibre; 6 g Protein; 446 mg Sodium

ABOUT LEBANESE YOGURT
Tangy strained yogurt, called *laban* or *labneh*, is a traditional food in Lebanon and throughout the Middle East. It's made by straining whole cow or goat milk yogurt through a cloth or paper filter to separate the solids from the whey. This process produces a creamy, cheese-like substance that is then mixed with a little salt and eaten fresh, used in cooking, or rolled into balls and preserved in olive oil.

SERVING SUGGESTION
This stew makes an excellent vegetarian entree, or an accompaniment to roast lamb or spicy grilled meats.

MAKE AHEAD
Prepare and refrigerate the three separate mixtures up to one day in advance, then reheat and assemble just before serving.

Comfort food with panache. This hearty dish is bursting with sharp, creamy yogurt, fresh mint, earthy pine nuts, and the complex sweetness of honey and tomato.

Eggplant Al Mihshi

Olive oil	1 tbsp.	15 mL
Finely chopped onion	1 cup	250 mL
Lebanese seven-spice blend	1 tsp.	5 mL
Vegetable broth	2/3 cup	150 mL
Bulgur, fine grind	1/4 cup	60 mL
Chopped pine nuts, toasted (see Tip, below)	1/4 cup	60 mL
Small oval or round eggplants	8	8
Tomato sauce	1 1/2 cups	375 mL
Chopped fresh parsley	2 tbsp.	30 mL

Heat olive oil in a saucepan on medium. Add onion and seven-spice blend and cook for 8 minutes until onion is softened.

Add broth and bring to a boil. Stir in bulgur and remove from heat. Let stand, covered, for 20 minutes until broth is absorbed.

Stir in pine nuts.

To stuff eggplants, cut a slit along one side about 2/3 of the way through and gently spread open. Fill with bulgur mixture. Arrange stuffed eggplants in a 2 quart (2 L) baking dish and pour tomato sauce over and around them. Cook, uncovered, in a 350°F (175°C) oven for 70 minutes until tender. Transfer to a serving plate and sprinkle with parsley. Makes 8 stuffed eggplants.

1 eggplant with 2 tbsp. (30 mL) sauce: 195 Calories; 5.7 g Total Fat (2.1 g Mono, 2.1 g Poly, 0.6 g Sat); 0 mg Cholesterol; 36 g Carbohydrate; 17 g Fibre; 7 g Protein; 304 mg Sodium

---

TIP

To toast nuts, seeds, whole spices or coconut, place them in an ungreased frying pan. Heat on medium for 3 to 5 minutes, stirring often, until golden. To bake, spread them evenly in an ungreased shallow pan. Bake in a 350°F (175°C) oven for 5 to 10 minutes, stirring or shaking often, until golden.

ABOUT MIHSHI DISHES

The word *mihshi* comes from the Arabic verb "to stuff." In Lebanese cuisine, stuffings generally contain some meat, rice and simple spices such as ground cinnamon, allspice and nutmeg.

All the **intense flavours** of Middle-Eastern **eggplant** dishes in an **elegant** presentation. A simple yet sophisticated stuffing of **spiced bulgur** and **buttery pine nuts** is tucked into these tiny eggplants.

Spice-Crusted Chicken Kabobs

Lemon juice	1/4 cup	60 mL
Garlic cloves, minced	8	8
Olive oil	2 tbsp.	30 mL
Ground allspice	1/2 tsp	2 mL
Cayenne pepper	1/8 tsp.	0.5 mL
Boneless, skinless chicken breast halves, cut into 1 inch (2.5 cm) pieces	1 1/2 lbs.	680 g
Bamboo skewers (8 inches, 20 cm, each), soaked in water for 10 minutes	8	8
Brown sugar, packed	1/3 cup	75 mL
Za'atar spice blend (see Tip, page 120)	1/3 cup	75 mL
Salt	1/4 tsp.	1 mL

Combine first 5 ingredients in a large resealable freezer bag. Add chicken and marinate in the refrigerator for at least 6 hours or overnight. Drain and discard marinade.

Thread chicken onto skewers. Combine remaining 3 ingredients in a shallow dish. Press chicken into za'atar mixture until coated on all sides. Cook on a greased grill on medium for 15 minutes, turning occasionally, until chicken is no longer pink inside. Makes 8 skewers.

1 skewer: 166 Calories; 4.6 g Total Fat (2.8 g Mono, 0.8 g Poly, 0.8 g Sat); 49 mg Cholesterol; 11 g Carbohydrate; trace Fibre; 20 g Protein; 132 mg Sodium

ABOUT LEBANESE WINE

Lebanon has been renowned for its wine since the times of the Phoenician traders. It is considered the oldest site of winemaking in the world; the Beqaa Valley was and continues to be the site of vineyards to this day. Wines are made mainly from French grapes, reds primarily from Cabernet Sauvignon and Cinsault grapes and whites from Chardonnay grapes. However, many whites are also made with a native grape called Obaideh, believed to be an ancient relative of Chardonnay. Production is relatively small and distribution is limited, so you may not find Lebanese wines at your local wine store. In that case, a full-bodied, lightly oaked Cabernet Sauvignon or Chardonnay should be a good accompaniment to this and many other Lebanese dishes.

SERVING SUGGESTION

This dish goes well with a simple salad of arugula that has been tossed in lemon juice, olive oil, salt and pepper and sprinkled with sliced grape tomatoes. For a decorative touch, add an attractively cut lemon wedge.

A sweet and herbaceous coating using the Lebanese staple spice blend za'atar replaces the pungent garlic sauce of the traditional *shish tawook* skewer. Tasty to eat, and fun to share.

Lamb Kibbe

Bulgur, fine grind	1 cup	250 mL
Lean ground lamb	1 lb.	500 g
Finely chopped onion	1 cup	250 mL
Ground allspice	1 tsp.	5 mL
Ground cinnamon	1/2 tsp.	2 mL
Salt	1 1/2 tsp.	7 mL
Pepper	1/2 tsp.	2 mL
Butter	1 tbsp.	15 mL
Chopped fresh parsley	1/4 cup	60 mL
Chopped fresh mint	1/4 cup	60 mL
Chopped tomato	1/3 cup	75 mL
Pine nuts, toasted (see Tip, page 128)	1/4 cup	60 mL

Cover bulgur with boiling water. Stir and let stand for 10 minutes. Drain well and transfer to a large mixing bowl.

Add next 6 ingredients and beat on low speed for 1 minute until mixture resembles a smooth paste. Press evenly in a greased 9 inch (22 cm) tart pan with a removable bottom (see Tip, below). Score 8 wedges into lamb mixture, about 1/2 inch (12 mm) deep.

Make a small indent in centre with finger and put butter into indent (see Why To, below). Bake on a foil-lined baking sheet in a 350°F (175°C) oven for 40 minutes until a meat thermometer reads 160°F (71°C). Let stand for 10 minutes before transferring to a serving plate.

Sprinkle remaining 4 ingredients, in order given, over top. Cuts into 8 wedges.

1 wedge: 225 Calories; 12.2 g Total Fat (4.4 g Mono, 2.2 g Poly, 4.3 g Sat); 41 mg Cholesterol; 17 g Carbohydrate; 4 g Fibre; 13 g Protein; 483 mg Sodium

ABOUT KIBBE (KIH-beh)
Kibbe is a considered one the national dishes of Lebanon. Myriad versions exist, including kibbe balls (*kibbe rass*), baked kibbe (*kibbe bin-saniyeh*) and even a version eaten raw like steak tartar (*kibbe nayeh*). There are also vegetarian and fish variations. The one ingredient that does not vary is bulgur (*burghul* in Lebanese). Our version is an elegant lamb pie with a fresh tomato and herb garnish.

TIP
Kibbe is traditionally kneaded by hand to give it the proper texture, but using a mixer with or without a paddle attachment also works very well. Be sure not to mix too fast or too long or the meat can become tough. Dampen your fingers with a little water to make pressing the meat mixture into the tart pan easier.

WHY TO
The butter-filled hole in the centre of the kibbe helps it to cook more evenly.

Transcend your idea of **comfort food.** Sumptuously **moist** from a hidden pocket of **melted butter** and scattered with **fresh herbs** and **tomato** for freshness, Lebanese kibbe is not your mother's meatloaf.

Shawarma Steak Sandwich

Pomegranate molasses	2 tbsp.	30 mL
Garlic cloves, minced	3	3
Ground allspice	1/2 tsp.	2 mL
Curry powder	1/4 tsp.	1 mL
Ground cinnamon	1/4 tsp.	1 mL
Salt	1/4 tsp.	1 mL
Pepper	1/4 tsp.	1 mL
Cayenne pepper	1/8 tsp.	0.5 mL
Beef strip loin steaks (1/2 lb., 225 g, each), 1 inch (2.5 cm) thick	2	2
Baguette bread loaf, split and cut into 4 pieces	1	1
Hummus	1/2 cup	125 mL
Tomato slices	16	16
English cucumber slices	16	16
Thinly sliced red onion	1/2 cup	125 mL

Combine first 8 ingredients in a large resealable freezer bag. Add steaks and marinate in the refrigerator for at least 6 hours or overnight. Drain and discard marinade. Cook steaks on a greased grill on medium-high for 5 minutes per side for medium-rare or until steaks reach desired doneness. Let stand, tented with foil, for 5 minutes.

Toast baguette on grill and spread with hummus. Slice steaks diagonally across the grain into thin slices and arrange on bread. Top with remaining 3 ingredients in order given. Makes 4 sandwiches.

1 sandwich: 464 Calories; 16.9 g Total Fat (6.3 g Mono, 1.7 g Poly, 5.2 g Sat); 67 mg Cholesterol; 49 g Carbohydrate; 6 g Fibre; 31 g Protein; 657 mg Sodium

ABOUT SHAWARMA

Shawarma is a favourite street food in Lebanon and other Middle Eastern countries. It's a sandwich made from thin strips of seasoned meat (lamb, goat, beef, chicken or turkey) that has been moulded onto a large, vertical rotisserie that turns in front of a gas or charcoal fire. The meat is shaved off to order and wrapped in a pita with various vegetables and a tahini, yogurt or hummus sauce. Versions of this same dish are called *gyro* in Greece and *doner kebab* in Turkey.

ABOUT POMEGRANATE MOLASSES

Pomegranate molasses is used in the marinade to promote a dark exterior that has a caramelized flavour. It should be available in Middle Eastern markets, but if you can't find it, make your own by boiling 3 cups (750 mL) of pomegranate juice until it's reduced to 1/2 cup (125 mL). Store in the refrigerator for up to two months in a sealed container.

A fabulously juicy **shawarma** with the pleasing **spices** and **crisp** charred edges of the real thing – without the need for a restaurant-sized **rotisserie**. A **baguette** takes the place of the traditional pita as a nod to the **French influences** in Lebanese cuisine.

Pistachio Baklava Cigars

Granulated sugar	1/2 cup	125 mL
Water	1/2 cup	125 mL
Orange blossom water	1 tbsp.	15 mL
Lemon juice	1 tbsp.	15 mL
Pistachios	1 1/4 cups	300 mL
Granulated sugar	1/2 cup	125 mL
Orange blossom water	2 tbsp.	30 mL
Ground cinnamon	1/2 tsp.	2 mL
Phyllo pastry sheets, thawed according to package directions	20	20
Melted butter	3/4 cup	175 mL

Heat and stir sugar and water in a saucepan on medium-high until sugar is dissolved. Bring to a boil. Stir in orange blossom water and lemon juice. Set aside to cool.

Process pistachios in a blender or food processor until finely chopped. Reserve 3 tbsp. (50 mL) for garnish. Add next 3 ingredients and process until mixture resembles a thick paste.

Layer 2 pastry sheets together with long side toward you, brushing each layer with melted butter. Keep remaining sheets covered with a damp tea towel. Cut into 3 rectangles (see How To, page 214). Spoon 1 1/2 tsp. (7 mL) filling along short edge of each rectangle. Fold long edges over filling and lay a drinking straw alongside filling. Roll up to enclose and push both ends toward centre to create a crinkled effect. Remove drinking straw. Repeat steps. Arrange rolls on a parchment paper-lined baking sheet. Bake in a 350°F (175°C) oven for 25 minutes until browned. Transfer baklava to a serving dish and drizzle with syrup. Sprinkle with reserved pistachios. Makes about 30 baklava.

1 baklava: 135 Calories; 7.8 g Total Fat (2.9 g Mono, 1.0 g Poly, 3.4 g Sat); 12 mg Cholesterol; 15 g Carbohydrate; 1 g Fibre; 2 g Protein; 94 mg Sodium

ABOUT LEBANESE COFFEE
In Lebanon, coffee is a symbol of hospitality, and is brewed following an elaborate process. Beans are dark roasted and freshly ground to a fine powder before being cooked in a long-handled, cone-shaped pot made of enamelware, brass or stainless steel (a *rakweh*). Water is brought to a boil in the pot, then the coffee and sugar are stirred in, 1 tsp. (5 mL) coffee plus 1/2 tsp. to 1 tsp. (2 mL to 5 mL) granulated sugar for each cup of water. The pot is set over low heat until the coffee foams up. It is then removed until the foam settles and the process is repeated two or three times until the foam disappears. It is then served very hot in small, narrow cups. Interestingly, coffee that is served at sad occasions or funerals is always prepared without sugar.

MAKE AHEAD
You can prepare and freeze these, in an airtight container, weeks in advance. Thaw and warm them slightly in the oven to crisp them before serving.

Perhaps the most sinfully sweet and delicious of Middle-Eastern desserts, baklava is available in a dazzling variety of shapes and flavours, including these simple yet decadent rolls with pistachio and orange blossom water.

Both the indigenous and the contemporary cuisines of Malaysia reveal blended Asian influences—historically, merchants wove through on sea trade routes leaving lasting culinary imprints, and today's thriving cities are cultural mosaics. Limes are often used in the cuisine, embodying the fun, welcoming and eclectic Malaysian spirit—for your fete, garnish chilled beverages with lime wedges, or display limes in a wooden bowl. Drape sheer fabric around your space for an exotic feel, and light candles in simple hurricane lamps.

Malaysian

Asian Fusion

Blossom Cups
With Jicama Shrimp Filling

Egg roll wrappers (8 inch, 20 cm, square), cut into quarters	6	6
Cooking oil	1/4 cup	60 mL
Sesame oil	1 tsp.	5 mL
Cooking oil	1 tsp.	5 mL
Uncooked shrimp (peeled and deveined), chopped	1/2 lb.	225 g
Finely grated ginger root	1 tsp.	5 mL
Garlic clove, minced	1	1
Julienned jicama	2 cups	500 mL
Julienned carrot	1 cup	250 mL
Sweet chili sauce	1 tbsp.	15 mL
Salt	1/4 tsp.	1 mL

Make 1 inch (2.5 cm) cuts halfway along each side of wrappers (see How To, page 214). Combine cooking and sesame oil and brush onto 1 side of wrappers. Press 12 wrappers, oil-side down, into 12 muffin cups. Press second wrapper, oil-side down, into each muffin cup, alternating points to form a flower shape. Bake in a 425°F (220°C) oven for 4 minutes until golden and crisp. Let stand in pan on wire rack for 5 minutes. Gently remove from pan.

Heat a wok or large frying pan on medium-high. Add cooking oil. Add next 3 ingredients and stir-fry for 1 minute until shrimp is pink. Transfer to a bowl.

Add remaining 4 ingredients to wok and stir-fry for 5 minutes until vegetables are tender-crisp. Return shrimp to wok and stir. Spoon into cups. Makes 12 cups.

1 cup: 113 Calories; 5.9 g Total Fat (2.9 g Mono, 1.6 g Poly, 0.5 g Sat); 29 mg Cholesterol; 10 g Carbohydrate; 2 g Fibre; 5 g Protein; 158 mg Sodium

GARNISH
thinly sliced small
  red chili pepper
thinly sliced green onion

ABOUT NONYA CUISINE
In the early 16th century, Chinese settlers immigrated to the straits of Singapore, Penang, and Malacca and many took Malaysian brides. The resulting blend of cultures created a culinary hybrid of Chinese and Malaysian ingredients and techniques. The people of this new culture became known as *Peranakan* and the women specifically as *Nonyas*. Over time the cuisine of the Peranakan became synonymous with the women who made it.

MAKE AHEAD
Make cups one to two days ahead and store in an airtight container. Serve at room temperature.

Delicate blossoms appear **innocuous**—but looks are deceiving. The **crisp wrappers** surround a blend of **shrimp**, crunchy **carrot** and **jicama** garnished with **fiery hot** peppers.

Spiced Pork and Coconut Fritters

Cooking oil	1 tbsp.	15 mL
Pork tenderloin, trimmed of fat, diced	3/4 lb.	340 g
Finely chopped shallots	1/3 cup	75 mL
Small red chili peppers, finely chopped (see Tip, page 148)	4	4
Garlic cloves, minced	2	2
Soy sauce	1 tbsp.	15 mL
Pepper	1/4 tsp.	1 mL
Large eggs	2	2
Coconut milk	1/2 cup	125 mL
Cooking oil	2 tbsp.	30 mL
All-purpose flour	1 cup	250 mL
Sweetened medium coconut, toasted (see Tip, page 128)	1/4 cup	60 mL
Granulated sugar	1 tbsp.	15 mL
Baking powder	1 1/2 tsp.	7 mL
Salt	1/2 tsp.	2 mL
Cooking oil	3/4 cup	175 mL

Heat a wok or large frying pan on medium. Add cooking oil. Add next 4 ingredients and stir-fry for 8 minutes until pork is no longer pink.

Stir in soy sauce and pepper and cool.

Whisk next 3 ingredients in a large bowl. Add next 5 ingredients and stir until combined. Add pork mixture and stir.

Heat 1/4 cup (60 mL) cooking oil in a large frying pan on medium (see Tip, page 26). Drop batter into pan, using about 2 tbsp. (30 mL) for each fritter. Shallow-fry for 2 minutes per side until browned. Remove to a paper towel-lined baking sheet and place in a 200°F (95°C) oven to keep warm. Repeat steps (see Tip, below). Makes about 26 fritters.

1 fritter: 119 Calories; 9.3 g Total Fat (4.5 g Mono, 2.2 g Poly, 1.8 g Sat); 25 mg Cholesterol; 6 g Carbohydrate; trace Fibre; 4 g Protein; 142 mg Sodium

---

GARNISH
shallots, cut into flowers
small red chili peppers

TIP
The pan will get hotter with each batch. Adjust the burner temperature accordingly.

MAKE AHEAD
Make and refrigerate fritters up to a day in advance. Reheat in 375°F (190°C) oven for 10 minutes until heated through.

Perfectly pleasing fritter cakes blend tender pork and toasted coconut in a light, crisp batter. Add a punch of freshness with a squeeze of lime to highlight the mild chili heat.

Malaysian Chicken Satay

Coconut milk	1/2 cup	125 mL
Thai peanut sauce	1/2 cup	125 mL
Cooking oil	1 tsp.	5 mL
Sambal belacan	1/2 tsp.	2 mL
Coconut milk	1/4 cup	60 mL
Brown sugar, packed	1 tbsp.	15 mL
Cooking oil	1 tsp.	5 mL
Brown sugar, packed	1 tbsp.	15 mL
Curry powder	1 tbsp.	15 mL
Finely grated ginger root	2 tsp.	10 mL
Garlic clove, minced	1	1
Salt	1/2 tsp.	2 mL
Boneless, skinless chicken thighs, halved lengthwise	1 lb.	454 g
Bamboo skewers (8 inches, 20 cm, each), soaked in water for 10 minutes	6	6

Combine coconut milk and peanut sauce. Heat cooking oil in a small saucepan on medium-high. Add sambal belacan and stir for 30 seconds until fragrant and bubbly. Add coconut milk mixture and stir for 2 minutes until boiling. Makes 1 cup (250 mL). Cool and refrigerate until ready to serve.

Stir next 3 ingredients in a small cup and refrigerate until ready to cook chicken.

Combine next 5 ingredients in a large resealable freezer bag. Add chicken and marinate in the refrigerator for 1 hour. Drain and discard marinade. Thread chicken onto skewers. Cook on a greased grill on medium-high for 8 minutes, turning and brushing with brown sugar mixture often, until no longer pink inside. Serve with peanut sauce mixture. Makes 6 skewers.

1 skewer with 1 tbsp. (15 mL) sauce: 246 Calories; 17.1 g Total Fat (3.4 g Mono, 1.8 g Poly, 7.8 g Sat); 50 mg Cholesterol; 8 g Carbohydrate; 1 g Fibre; 16 g Protein; 635 mg Sodium

GARNISH
chopped cilantro
shredded coconut, toasted

ABOUT COCONUT IN MALAYSIAN COOKING
The flavour of coconut can come to your kitchen in many forms—coconut water, oil, meat and milk are all widely used in Malaysian cooking. In particular, coconut milk is coveted for its ability to mellow fiery flavours and add richness to curries and soups.

SERVING SUGGESTION
Serve with a vibrant assortment of fresh vegetables, such as red pepper, cucumber and jicama. The refreshing flavours of the vegetables will help to ease the heat between bites of satay.

MAKE AHEAD
The peanut sauce can be made up to three days in advance. Refrigerate until needed, and warm before serving. Basting sauce can also be prepared in advance. Refrigerate until needed.

Nothing enlivens a party like **fabulous skewers** for sharing—
fragrantly **spicy chicken** enrobed in creamy **peanut satay**
sauce is something to celebrate.

Belacan Sambal Vegetables

Ingredient	Imperial	Metric
Chopped shallots (see Tip, below)	1/2 cup	125 mL
Chili paste (sambal oelek)	2 tsp.	10 mL
Cooking oil	2 tsp.	10 mL
Shrimp paste (belacan)	1 tsp.	5 mL
Garlic cloves, chopped	2	2
Salt	1/4 tsp.	1 mL
Cooking oil	1 tbsp.	15 mL
Chopped long beans, cut into 2 inch (5 cm) pieces	3 cups	750 mL
Chopped Asian eggplant, cut into 1 1/2 inch (3.8 cm) pieces	2 1/2 cups	625 mL
Water	2 tbsp.	30 mL
Brown sugar, packed	1 tbsp.	15 mL
Lime juice	1 tsp.	5 mL
Chopped, seeded Roma (plum) tomato	1/4 cup	60 mL

Process first 6 ingredients in a blender or food processor until mixture resembles a paste.

Heat a wok or large frying pan on medium-high. Add cooking oil. Add beans and eggplant and stir-fry for 4 minutes until eggplant starts to soften. Transfer to a bowl and cover to keep warm.

Reduce heat to medium, add paste to wok and stir-fry for 1 minute. Add next 3 ingredients and eggplant mixture and stir-fry for 4 minutes until vegetables are almost tender.

Add tomato and stir-fry for 1 minute. Makes about 3 1/2 cups (875 mL).

1/2 cup (125 mL): 255 Calories; 4.2 g Total Fat (2.0 g Mono, 1.3 g Poly, 0.5 g Sat); 0 mg Cholesterol; 42 g Carbohydrate; 8 g Fibre; 15 g Protein; 126 mg Sodium

TIP
If shallots aren't available, you can substitute an onion instead. You can also substitute fresh green beans for long beans.

ABOUT SAMBAL
Sambal refers to a condiment that's made from a variety of chili peppers. There are numerous variations of sambal, ranging from spicy to sweet.

SERVING SUGGESTION
Most Asian cultures appreciate balance. This principle extends to lifestyle and food as well. To create a balance with this stir-fry, serve it with a curry and a grilled dish.

Chili and Asparagus Stir-Fry

Brown sugar, packed	1 tbsp.	15 mL
Lime juice	1 tbsp.	15 mL
Chili paste (sambal oelek)	1 tsp.	5 mL
Salt	1/4 tsp.	1 mL
Cooking oil	1 tbsp.	15 mL
Asparagus, trimmed of tough ends and cut into 2 inch (5 cm) pieces (see Tip, below)	1 lb.	454 g
Finely sliced small red chili peppers (see Tip, below)	2 tsp.	10 mL

Combine first 4 ingredients.

Heat a wok or large frying pan on medium-high. Add cooking oil. Add chili paste mixture and stir-fry for 30 seconds until fragrant. Add asparagus and stir-fry for 4 minutes until tender-crisp.

Transfer to a serving dish and sprinkle with chili pepper. Makes about 2 cups (500 mL).

1/2 cup (125 mL): 67 Calories; 3.7 g Total Fat (2.0 g Mono, 1.1 g Poly, 0.3 g Sat); 0 mg Cholesterol; 8 g Carbohydrate; 2 g Fibre; 3 g Protein; 176 mg Sodium

---

TIP

Traditionally, this dish is made with the seasonal vegetable water spinach. Unlike Western spinach, water spinach is always eaten cooked.

TIP

Hot peppers contain capsaicin in the seeds and ribs. Removing the seeds and ribs will reduce the heat. Wear rubber gloves when handling hot peppers and avoid touching your eyes. Wash your hands well afterwards.

SERVING SUGGESTION

This simple dish pairs well with other Malaysian and Southeast Asian dishes, such as steamed fish or curry. Variations of this stir-fry are found in Thailand, Taiwan, Singapore, Vietnam, China, Indonesia and Philippines, each with its own twist.

Experience a **flavourful** fusion.
Asparagus is not native to Asia, yet easily lends
its **tender-crisp** qualities to a **spicy** stir-fry adorned with
vibrant red chili peppers.

Butternut Squash Curry

Cooking oil	1 tbsp.	15 mL
Brown mustard seed	2 tsp.	10 mL
Fennel seed	1 tsp.	5 mL
Chopped onion	1 1/3 cups	325 mL
Salt	1/2 tsp.	2 mL
Chopped butternut squash (1 inch, 2.5 cm, pieces)	1 1/2 lbs.	680 g
Curry powder	1 tbsp.	15 mL
Whole green cardamom, bruised	4	4
Prepared vegetable broth	1 1/2 cups	375 mL
Brown sugar, packed	2 tbsp.	30 mL
Lime juice	1 tbsp.	15 mL

Heat a wok or large frying pan on medium-high. Add cooking oil. Add mustard and fennel seed and stir for 2 minutes until seeds pop (see Why To, below).

Add onion and salt and stir-fry for 5 minutes until onion is golden brown.

Add next 3 ingredients and stir until coated. Add broth and bring to a boil. Reduce heat to medium-low and cook, uncovered, for 1 hour, stirring occasionally, until squash is tender and liquid is thickened. Discard cardamom pods.

Stir sugar and lime into squash mixture. Makes about 4 cups (1 L).

1/2 cup (125 mL): 91 Calories; 2.3 g Total Fat (1.2 g Mono, 0.6 g Poly, 0.2 g Sat); 0 mg Cholesterol; 18 g Carbohydrate; 3 g Fibre; 2 g Protein; 238 mg Sodium

---

GARNISH
cilantro leaves

ABOUT SQUASH IN ASIAN COOKING
In Asian recipes, the word *pumpkin* can refer to a number of winter squash, but not the large orange pumpkins that are associated with Halloween. Small pie pumpkins and acorn or buttercup squash can be used in this dish, but we have selected butternut squash for its delightfully sweet flavour and widespread availability.

WHY TO
Toasting whole spices in oil helps to bring out the flavour and essential oils inside. Ground spices should be cooked only briefly before liquid is added to prevent any bitterness that can result from overcooking.

SERVING SUGGESTION
Serve with a hot and spicy meat dish or fish curry—and rice, of course!

This mild curry dish provides a balance for the richer offerings on your table. Butternut squash and browned onions bring a delightfully sweet flavour, while flecks of mustard seed add a festive appearance.

Grilled Spiced Chicken

Chopped shallots	1/4 cup	60 mL
Soy sauce	1/4 cup	60 mL
Tamarind liquid (see How To, page 212)	1/4 cup	60 mL
Brown sugar, packed	3 tbsp.	50 mL
Chopped galangal (see Tip, below)	2 tbsp.	30 mL
Small red chili peppers, chopped (see Tip, page 148)	4	4
Garlic cloves	3	3
Lemon grass, bulbs only, sliced	2	2
Boneless, skinless chicken breast halves (4 – 6 oz., 113 – 170 g, each)	4	4

Process first 8 ingredients in a blender or food processor until smooth and pour into a large resealable freezer bag.

Add chicken and marinate in the refrigerator for 4 hours. Drain marinade into a small saucepan and bring to a boil. Reduce heat to medium and gently boil for 5 minutes. Cook chicken on a greased grill for 8 minutes per side, brushing with marinade occasionally, until a meat thermometer reads 170°F (77°C). Let stand, tented with foil, for 5 minutes. Cut into slices to serve. Makes 4 breasts.

1 breast: 240 Calories; 1.8 g Total Fat (0.4 g Mono, 0.5 g Poly, 0.4 g Sat); 66 mg Cholesterol; 28 g Carbohydrate; 1 g Fibre; 29 g Protein; 1402 mg Sodium

ABOUT GALANGAL (guh-LANG-guhl)
This root gives a peppery-ginger flare, and is commonly used as a substitute for ginger. Galangal has a milder and more floral taste that goes well with many cornerstone ingredients of Southeast Asian cooking, such as lime, basil and lemon grass.

TIP
If you cannot find galangal, use ginger root as a substitute. Since galangal is milder than ginger root, reduce the amount by about half.

MAKE AHEAD
Chicken can be marinated in the refrigerator overnight.

GARNISH
butter lettuce leaves
small red chili peppers

Familiar-seeming fare with an **extraordinary** taste. Moist slices of **grilled chicken** steeped in a **soy** and **tamarind** marinade offer hints of **citrus** and **chilli**. Round out the dish with a bed of **bean sprouts** and cool **cucumber**.

Beef Rendang

Fine coconut, toasted (see Tip, page 128)	1/2 cup	125 mL
Brown sugar, packed	2 tbsp.	30 mL
Chopped onion	1 cup	250 mL
Lemon grass, bulbs only, thinly sliced	2	2
Chopped galangal (see Tip, page 152)	2 tbsp.	30 mL
Chopped ginger root	2 tbsp.	30 mL
Cooking oil	2 tbsp.	30 mL
Chopped garlic	1 tbsp.	15 mL
Finely chopped small red chili pepper (see Tip, page 148)	2 tsp.	10 mL
Ground coriander	2 tsp.	10 mL
Ground cumin	2 tsp.	10 mL
Ground cardamom	1 tsp.	5 mL
Cooking oil	1 tbsp.	15 mL
Boneless beef cross-rib roast, cut into 1 inch (2.5 cm) pieces	2 lbs.	900 g
Coconut milk	2 cups	500 mL
Lemon grass, bulb only, bruised	1	1
Lime leaves	2	2
Salt	1 tsp.	5 mL

Process coconut and sugar in a blender or food processor until mixture resembles fine crumbs and set aside.

Process next 10 ingredients until mixture resembles a paste.

Heat cooking oil in a Dutch oven on medium. Add paste and stir-fry for 2 minutes until fragrant. Add beef and stir-fry for 7 minutes until coated and starting to brown.

Add remaining 4 ingredients. Stir until mixture comes to a boil. Reduce heat to medium-low and simmer, uncovered, stirring frequently, for 2 hours until beef is very tender and sauce is thickened. Discard lemon grass bulb and lime leaves. Stir in coconut crumb mixture. Makes about 4 cups (1 L).

1/2 cup (125 mL): 582 Calories; 51.8 g Total Fat (17.3 g Mono, 2.8 g Poly, 26.7 g Sat); 74 mg Cholesterol; 12 g Carbohydrate; 2 g Fibre; 20 g Protein; 357 mg Sodium

ABOUT LIME LEAVES
The aroma of lime leaves is unique and more flavourful than those of other citrus fruits, making this ingredient a sought-after choice for Southeast Asian cooking. Some grocery stores may sell frozen lime leaves, but you can also find the fresh leaves at many Asian markets.

GARNISH
lime leaves
small red chili peppers

A classic south-Asian dish, this beef entree is rich with ginger and coconut—perfect for serving over coconut rice or with flatbread. Lime leaves and lemon grass create an unexpected freshness.

Malaysian Fish Curry

Chopped shallots	2/3 cup	150 mL
Chopped ginger root	2 tbsp.	30 mL
Cooking oil	1 tbsp.	15 mL
Garlic cloves, chopped	2	2
Chili paste (sambal oelek)	1 tsp.	5 mL
Cooking oil	1 tbsp.	15 mL
Lemon grass bulbs, bruised	2	2
Fennel seed, crushed	1 tsp.	5 mL
Mustard seed, crushed	1 tsp.	5 mL
Can of coconut milk	14 oz.	398 mL
Tamarind liquid (see How To, page 212)	3 tbsp.	50 mL
Chopped Asian eggplant	2 cups	500 mL
(1 inch, 2.5 cm pieces)		
Fresh (or frozen, thawed) whole okra,	4 oz.	113 g
halved crosswise		
Red snapper fillets, cut into	3/4 lb.	340 g
1 inch (2.5 cm) pieces		
Granulated sugar	1 tsp.	5 mL
Seafood bouillon powder	1 tsp.	5 mL
Salt	1/4 tsp.	1 mL

Process first 5 ingredients in a blender or food processor until mixture resembles a paste.

Heat cooking oil in a large saucepan on medium. Add next 3 ingredients and stir for 2 minutes until fragrant. Add paste and stir for 2 minutes until fragrant.

Add coconut milk and tamarind liquid and bring to a boil. Add eggplant and okra and simmer, uncovered, for 10 minutes until almost tender.

Add remaining 4 ingredients and simmer for 5 minutes until fish flakes easily when tested with a fork. Discard lemon grass. Makes about 3 3/4 cups (925 mL).

1/2 cup (125 mL): 216 Calories; 16.0 g Total Fat (2.8 g Mono, 1.4 g Poly, 10.5 g Sat); 17 mg Cholesterol; 9 g Carbohydrate; 2 g Fibre; 12 g Protein; 266 mg Sodium

ABOUT ASIAN EGGPLANT
Asian eggplant is actually a term used to identify a variety of eggplant grown all over Asia. Japanese and Chinese eggplant is the long, purple variety that's commonly used in stir-fries. Thai eggplants are more stout and actually resemble eggs. No matter where in Asia it's grown, Asian eggplant is generally sweeter and more tender than the slightly bitter and firm Western varieties.

GARNISH
sliced lemon grass
small red chili peppers

Infused with coconut and ginger heat, this is a delightfully unusual blend with pleasing bites of red snapper, eggplant and okra. A saucy delight to serve atop steamy rice.

Grilled Tilapia in Banana Leaf

Lemon grass paste	2 tbsp.	30 mL
Lime juice	2 tbsp.	30 mL
Brown sugar, packed	1 tbsp.	15 mL
Sambal belacan	1 tbsp.	15 mL
Salt	1 tsp.	5 mL
Garlic cloves, minced	3	3
Banana leaf	1	1
Tilapia fillets (4 – 5 oz., 113 – 140 g, each)	4	4
Sliced fresh Thai basil	1 tbsp.	15 mL
Finely sliced small red chili pepper (see Tip, page 148)	1 tbsp.	15 mL

Combine first 6 ingredients.

Place a large sheet of aluminum foil on work surface. Lay banana leaf, shiny side down, on foil. Arrange fillets in centre of leaf and spread lemon grass mixture over fillets (see How To, page 215). Bring up sides of leaf and fold over to enclose. Wrap tightly in foil.

Cook fish on an ungreased grill on medium for 10 minutes until fish flakes easily when tested with a fork. Remove foil and transfer fish in banana leaf to a serving platter.

Sprinkle fillets with basil and chili pepper. Makes 4 fillets.

1 serving: 153 Calories; 2.9 g Total Fat (0.6 g Mono, 0.5 g Poly, 0.7 g Sat); 57 mg Cholesterol; 8 g Carbohydrate; trace Fibre; 23 g Protein; 931 mg Sodium

ABOUT BANANA LEAVES
The large leaves of the banana plant provide versatile applications for Asian cuisine. These leaves can be used as a plate, a serving cup, or as a wrapper for food to be cooked in. Banana leaves can be purchased frozen in some large grocery stores or Asian markets. Fresh banana leaves need to be dipped in boiling water to soften enough for folding, but frozen leaves can simply be thawed and used.

GARNISH
lime wedges
small red chili peppers

Vibrant presentation melds with **fabulous** flavour. **Banana leaves** offer a delicate herbal note to **citrus-steeped** tilapia, speckled with sliced **chili peppers** and Thai basil.

Jackfruit Mousse

Can of jackfruit (with syrup)	20 oz.	565 mL
Granulated sugar	1/4 cup	60 mL
Unflavoured gelatin	2 tsp.	10 mL
Egg yolks (large)	4	4
Granulated sugar	1/4 cup	60 mL
Lemon juice	1 tbsp.	15 mL
Water	1 tbsp.	15 mL
Whipped cream	1 cup	250 mL

Process jackfruit and sugar in a blender or food processor until smooth and pour into a saucepan. Sprinkle gelatin over jackfruit mixture and let stand for 1 minute. Heat and stir on medium until gelatin is dissolved. Set aside.

Whisk next 4 ingredients in a medium stainless steel bowl. Set over simmering water in a large saucepan so that bottom of bowl is not touching water (see How To, page 215). Whisk for 15 minutes until mixture is thickened and doubled in volume (see Why To, below). Remove from heat and fold in jackfruit mixture. Chill for 2 hours, stirring once or twice, until almost set.

Fold in whipped cream. Spoon or pipe into 6 glasses or bowls and chill for 4 hours or overnight. Serves 6.

1 serving: 315 Calories; 17.6 g Total Fat (5.5 g Mono, 1.0 g Poly, 10.2 g Sat); 191 mg Cholesterol; 36 g Carbohydrate; 1 g Fibre; 3 g Protein; 29 mg Sodium

ABOUT JACKFRUIT
This large relative of the fig is native to parts of Brazil, Africa and Southeast Asia. This slightly sweet fruit pairs well with curry and makes for a refreshing dessert. In North America, jackfruit is only available canned.

WHY TO
Using a sabayon method rather than whipped egg whites to form the mousse, results in a light texture and eliminates the risk from eating raw eggs.

MAKE AHEAD
Make and refrigerate mousse up to two days in advance.

Spoon into sunny sweetness: this smooth,
pale yellow mousse balances a light frothiness with
the appealing texture of jackfruit.

Even in the sweltering tropics, Thailand's cuisine is renowned for its fiery dishes. Intriguingly, hot and spicy food helps keep you cool in the intense heat. Thai dishes perform a complex balancing act between the characteristic flavours of hot, sour, salty and sweet—evident in everything from rich curries to simple salads. Gather guests for a sumptuous Thai-style banquet, inviting a tropical feel with bamboo mats and a colourful silk runner down your table. At every seat, place a cup with a single floating orchid.

Thai

Tropical Heat

Basil Salad Rolls

Rice vermicelli	2 oz.	57 g
Coarsely chopped salted cashews	1/3 cup	75 mL
Grated carrot	1/4 cup	60 mL
Julienned yellow pepper	1/4 cup	60 mL
Julienned English cucumber	3 tbsp.	50 mL
Thinly sliced green onion	2 tbsp.	30 mL
Rice paper rounds (6 inch, 15 cm, diameter)	10	10
Fresh Thai basil leaves	30	30
Water	1/4 cup	60 mL
Granulated sugar	2 tbsp.	30 mL
Fish sauce	4 tsp.	20 mL
Garlic clove, minced	1	1
Chili paste (sambal oelek)	1/2 tsp.	2 mL

Cover vermicelli with boiling water and let stand until just tender. Drain and rinse under cold water. Drain well and transfer to a large bowl. Cut noodles in half twice.

Add next 5 ingredients and toss.

Place 1 rice paper round in a shallow bowl of hot water until just softened (see Tip, page 190). Place on work surface. Arrange 3 basil leaves in centre of rice paper. Spoon about 1/4 cup (60 mL) vermicelli mixture over basil. Fold sides over filling and roll up from bottom to enclose (see How To, page 215). Repeat steps.

Stir remaining 5 ingredients until sugar is dissolved. Makes about 1/3 cup (75 mL) dipping sauce. Serve with salad rolls. Makes 10 rolls.

1 roll with 1 1/2 tsp. (7 mL) sauce: 125 Calories; 2.8 g Total Fat (0 g Mono, trace Poly, 0.6 g Sat); 0 mg Cholesterol; 23 g Carbohydrate; 1 g Fibre; 2 g Protein; 339 mg Sodium

ABOUT THAI BASIL
There are three common varieties of Thai basil, but the most popular is *horapa*, which has a mild licorice flavour and smaller leaves than Western basil.

ABOUT SALAD ROLLS
Salad rolls are distinct from other roll-type appetizers such as spring and egg rolls in that they are not fried or deep fried. They're made with fresh herbs, rice vermicelli and cooked shrimp or other meats, and are served cold or at room temperature. They can be eaten as a light meal as well as an appetizer. This recipe is a vegetarian version.

GARNISH
sprigs of Thai basil

A lovely union of tender and crisp, these packages make for delightful dipping. Verdant Thai basil leaves are visible through luminescent rice paper.

Chili Cilantro Shrimp Skewers

Chopped fresh cilantro	1/4 cup	60 mL
Cooking oil	3 tbsp.	50 mL
Lime juice	3 tbsp.	50 mL
Fish sauce	2 tbsp.	30 mL
Garlic cloves, minced	3	3
Small red chili peppers, finely chopped (see Tip, page 148)	2	2
Uncooked large shrimp (peeled and deveined), tails intact	36	36
Bamboo skewers (8 inches, 20 cm, each), soaked in water for 10 minutes	12	12

Process first 6 ingredients in a blender or food processor until smooth. Pour marinade into a large resealable freezer bag, reserving 1/4 cup (60 mL). Add shrimp and marinate in the refrigerator for 20 minutes. Drain and discard marinade.

Thread 3 shrimp onto 1 end of each skewer (see How To, below). Cook skewers on a greased grill on high for 6 minutes, turning and brushing with reserved marinade occasionally, until pink. Serve with sweet chili sauce. Makes 12 skewers.

1 skewer: 58 Calories; 3.9 g Total Fat (2.1 g Mono, 1.2 g Poly, 0.3 g Sat); 32 mg Cholesterol; 2 g Carbohydrate; trace Fibre; 5 g Protein; 264 mg Sodium

---

GARNISH
lime wedges
cilantro leaves
small red chili peppers

TIP
The dish can be made hotter by adding another chili to the marinade.

HOW TO SKEWER SHRIMP
Thread skewers through the head and tail of shrimp, leaving a little space between each one to ensure even grilling.

Simply sophisticated, casual chic.
These grilled shrimp bites are tender, spicy and sweet,
with a hint of smoke that lingers and lures.

Crispy Cilantro Fish Cakes

Large egg	1	1
Chopped fresh cilantro	3 tbsp.	50 mL
Fish sauce	1 tbsp.	15 mL
Thai red curry paste	2 tsp.	10 mL
Garlic cloves, minced	3	3
Salt	1/4 tsp.	1 mL
Pepper	1/2 tsp.	2 mL
Haddock fillets (see Tip, below), coarsely chopped	3/4 lb.	340 g
Panko crumbs	1/2 cup	125 mL
Panko crumbs	1/2 cup	125 mL
Cooking oil	1 cup	250 mL

Process first 7 ingredients in a blender or food processor until just combined.

Add fish and process until coarsely ground. Transfer to a medium bowl, add panko crumbs and mix well. Form into 1 inch (2.5 cm) balls and flatten into patties.

Press patties into panko crumbs until coated. Heat cooking oil in a large frying pan on medium-high (see Tip, page 26). Shallow-fry patties in 2 batches for 1 to 2 minutes per side until browned. Transfer to paper towels to drain. Makes about 26 fish cakes.

1 cake: 39 Calories; 2.5 g Total Fat (1.3 g Mono, 0.7 g Poly, 0.3 g Sat); 16 mg Cholesterol; 1 g Carbohydrate; trace Fibre; 3 g Protein; 104 mg Sodium

ABOUT PANKO CRUMBS
These are generally used for coating fried foods in Asian cooking. Because they tend to be coarser than the bread crumbs used in North American cuisine, they create a perfectly crunchy crust.

TIP
Types of fish typically used for fish cakes include mullet, mackerel or John Dory. John Dory is preferred because of its firm texture and mild sweetness, but any type of firm white fish can be used. We used haddock because of its availability.

MAKE AHEAD
Make and refrigerate the cakes up to one day in advance. Reheat in 375°F (190°C) oven for about eight minutes until heated through.

GARNISH
lime wedges
cilantro leaves

A squeeze of lime brightens the curry and garlic flavour in these delicate cakes. Golden-crisp on the outside, soft and moist on the inside.

Glass Noodle Vegetable Salad

Bean thread noodles	3 oz.	85 g
Bean sprouts, trimmed	2 cups	500 mL
Can of shoestring-style bamboo shoots, drained	8 oz.	227 mL
Julienned carrot	1/2 cup	125 mL
Julienned English cucumber	1/2 cup	125 mL
Julienned mango	1/2 cup	125 mL
Thinly sliced red pepper	1/2 cup	125 mL
Chopped fresh cilantro	1/4 cup	60 mL
Thinly sliced green onion	1/4 cup	60 mL
Lime juice	1/4 cup	60 mL
Fish sauce	3 tbsp.	50 mL
Brown sugar, packed	3 tbsp.	50 mL
Dried crushed chilies	1 tsp.	5 mL

Cover noodles with hot water and let stand for 15 minutes until tender. Drain well and put into a large bowl.

Add next 8 ingredients and toss.

Whisk remaining 4 ingredients until sugar is dissolved. Drizzle over noodle mixture and toss. Let stand, covered, for 30 minutes before serving. Makes about 5 cups (1.25 L).

1 cup (250 mL): 159 Calories; 0.6 g Total Fat (0.1 g Mono, 0.1 g Poly, 0.1 g Sat); 0 mg Cholesterol; 38 g Carbohydrate; 3 g Fibre; 4 g Protein; 894 mg Sodium

ABOUT BEAN THREAD NOODLES
Known by many names, including *cellophane noodles* and *glass noodles*, these noodles get their translucent appearance from the starch of mung beans. In most recipes, bean thread noodles must be soaked before they are used.

ABOUT THAI SALADS
Thai salads are known for having distinct textures, incorporating such diverse ingredients as squid, oysters, duck, fruit, vegetables and fresh herbs. Dressings may combine lime, chilies, garlic, sugar and fish sauce, flavours that are strong and complex but whose function it is to balance out and unify the salad ingredients. Thai salads can be eaten on their own and are versatile enough to be enjoyed at any time of the day.

GARNISH
lime slices

Opaque **bean thread** noodles and colourful,
thinly sliced **vegetables** are dressed with a ubiquitous **salty,**
tangy, sour and **hot** dressing. A **dynamic** interplay
of colour, flavour and texture.

Pomelo Salad

With Shrimp and Chicken

Lime juice	1/4 cup	60 mL
Fish sauce	4 tsp.	20 mL
Brown sugar, packed	1 tbsp.	15 mL
Finely chopped small red chili pepper (see Tip, page 148)	2 tsp.	10 mL
Garlic clove, minced	1	1
Pomelos, peeled and segmented	2	2
Cooked medium shrimp (peeled and deveined)	12	12
Diced cooked chicken breast	1 cup	250 mL
Chopped fresh mint	1/3 cup	75 mL
Thinly sliced shallots	1/4 cup	60 mL
Chopped fresh cilantro	1 tbsp.	15 mL
Shredded coconut, toasted (see Tip, page 128)	2 tbsp.	30 mL

Combine first 5 ingredients in a large bowl.

Add next 6 ingredients and toss gently to combine. Transfer to a serving plate.

Sprinkle with coconut. Makes about 4 cups (1 L).

1 cup (250 mL): 159 Calories; 2.7 g Total Fat (0.1 g Mono, 0.2 g Poly, 1.0 g Sat); 57 mg Cholesterol; 17 g Carbohydrate; 1 g Fibre; 18 g Protein; 768 mg Sodium

ABOUT POMELOS

Also known as *Chinese grapefruit*, the pomelo is similar to grapefruit in taste, though pomelos have a much thicker skin. Pomelos come in pink and white varieties and vary in taste and texture. Look for those that are heavy for their size and unblemished. If you can't find pomelos, two large grapefruit can be substituted in this recipe.

PRESENTATION INSPIRATION

For a more authentic experience, serve extra dressing ingredients in individual bowls on the table so guests can play with the flavour elements to their taste. Achieving a balance between sweet, sour, salty and hot flavours is key.

Pique your guests' interest. This **unique** salad—**tart**, **sweet, salty** and **fresh**—is as enticing and eclectic as Thai **culture** itself.

Tom Yum Shrimp Soup

Water	4 cups	1 L
Lemon grass, bulbs only, bruised and chopped	2	2
Lime leaves	5	5
Thin slices of galangal (see Tip, page 152)	5	5
Small red chili peppers, finely chopped (see Tip, page 148)	3	3
Uncooked medium shrimp (peeled and deveined)	3/4 lb.	340 g
Thinly sliced fresh shiitake mushrooms	1 cup	250 mL
Lime juice	3 tbsp.	50 mL
Fish sauce	1 tbsp.	15 mL
Salt	1/2 tsp.	2 mL

Combine first 5 ingredients in a large saucepan and bring to a boil. Reduce heat to medium and gently boil for 5 minutes until fragrant.

Add shrimp and mushrooms. Heat and stir for 3 minutes until shrimp turn pink. Remove from heat and stir in remaining 3 ingredients. Makes about 5 cups (1.25 L).

1 cup (250 mL): 113 Calories; 1.4 g Total Fat (0.2 g Mono, 0.6 g Poly, 0.3 g Sat); 103 mg Cholesterol; 11 g Carbohydrate; 1 g Fibre; 15 g Protein; 614 mg Sodium

ABOUT LEMON GRASS

This staple of Thai cuisine is an essential ingredient for adding a light lemon flavour to soups, teas and other dishes. Lemon grass can be purchased either fresh or dried.

ABOUT TOM YUM SOUP

This robustly flavoured Thai soup is of the classic salty, sour and hot variety. Tom yum soup can be made hotter or milder depending on the spice level of the other dishes served in the meal. Its bright, sharp, citrus flavour pairs well with many dishes, especially spicy curries.

MAKE AHEAD

This soup does not lend itself well to advance preparation. Thai soups emphasize fresh, intense flavours, so make it just before you plan to serve it, and add fresh lime and fish sauce at the table. It's very easy to throw together at the last minute.

The perfume of galangal and lime rises from this cloudy broth. Tender shrimp and earthy mushrooms linger below the surface. Heady flavours and a welcome heat animate the palate.

Pad Thai

Medium rice stick noodles	1/2 lb.	225 g
Brown sugar, packed	3 tbsp.	50 mL
Fish sauce	3 tbsp.	50 mL
Lime juice	3 tbsp.	50 mL
Tamarind liquid (see How To, page 212)	3 tbsp.	50 mL
Soy sauce	2 tbsp.	30 mL
Chili paste (sambal oelek)	1 tbsp.	15 mL
Pepper	1/2 tsp.	2 mL
Cooking oil	3 tbsp.	50 mL
Uncooked extra-large shrimp (peeled and deveined)	1 lb.	454 g
Sliced green onion	1/4 cup	60 mL
Garlic cloves, thinly sliced	3	3
Large eggs	2	2
Bean sprouts, trimmed	2 cups	500 mL
Cilantro leaves	12	12
Unsalted peanuts, coarsely chopped	1/4 cup	60 mL
Dried crushed chilies	1/8 tsp.	0.5 mL

Cover noodles with warm water and let stand for 30 minutes until softened. Drain well and set aside.

Combine next 7 ingredients and set aside.

Heat a wok or large frying pan on medium-high. Add cooking oil. Add next 3 ingredients and stir-fry for 2 minutes until shrimp just turn pink. Transfer to a plate and cover to keep warm.

Add eggs to wok and break yolks. Cook, without stirring, until partially set. Stir-fry until set. Add bean sprouts, fish sauce mixture and noodles and toss until coated. Add shrimp mixture and stir-fry for 3 minutes until heated through. Transfer to a serving plate.

Sprinkle with remaining 3 ingredients in order given. Makes about 8 cups (2 L).

1 cup (250 mL): 309 Calories; 9.9 g Total Fat (4.4 g Mono, 2.7 g Poly, 1.3 g Sat); 140 mg Cholesterol; 38 g Carbohydrate; 2 g Fibre; 18 g Protein; 1048 mg Sodium

GARNISH
green onion frills
lime wedges

ABOUT THAI CULINARY ARTS
The walled city known as the Grand Palace in Bangkok was the Thai king's official residence and the seat of government for 150 years, from the 18th to the mid-20th centuries. Within its busy network of streets, houses, shops and gardens some 3000 women, mainly the daughters of noble families, lived out their lives, acquiring refined and elegant food preparation skills such as fruit and vegetable carving. As a result of their training in elaborate food preparation, these women helped to establish cuisine as a part of Thailand's high culture. To this day, many fine Thai restaurants boast chefs whose mothers were educated at the royal residence.

This signature dish dazzles. Tender **shrimp**, fettuccini-style **rice noodles** and crunchy **peanuts** are nestled in a **noteworthy sauce**—a perfectly balanced interplay of sweetness, spice and tang with a **peppery** finish.

Coconut Pork Curry

Fish sauce	2 tbsp.	30 mL
Brown sugar, packed	1 tbsp.	15 mL
Cornstarch	2 tsp.	10 mL
Cooking oil	1 tbsp.	15 mL
Pork tenderloin, trimmed of fat, thinly sliced (see Tip, page 208)	1 lb.	454 g
Tom yum paste	2 tbsp.	30 mL
Garlic cloves, thinly sliced	3	3
Thai green curry paste	1 tbsp.	15 mL
Turmeric	1/2 tsp.	2 mL
Can of coconut milk	14 oz.	398 mL
Fresh Thai basil leaves	12	12
Lime leaves	4	4

Stir first 3 ingredients until smooth and set aside.

Heat a wok or large frying pan on medium-high. Add cooking oil. Add pork and stir-fry in 2 batches for 2 minutes until starting to brown. Transfer to a plate and cover to keep warm.

Add next 4 ingredients to wok and stir-fry for 30 seconds until fragrant.

Add remaining 3 ingredients and bring to a boil. Stir in fish sauce mixture until boiling and thickened. Return pork to wok and stir for 1 minute until hot. Makes about 3 cups (750 mL).

1/2 cup (125 mL): 325 Calories; 25.6 g Total Fat (3.1 g Mono, 1.1 g Poly, 15.3 g Sat); 49 mg Cholesterol; 9 g Carbohydrate; 2 g Fibre; 18 g Protein; 889 mg Sodium

---

GARNISH
lime leaves
small red chili peppers

MAKE AHEAD
Make, cool and refrigerate this dish up to one day in advance. Reheat to serve.

This **earthy** and **exotic, richly flavoured** sauce will transport dinner guests. **Medium heat** and **citrus overtones** appeal to the indulgent.

Bangkok Basa

Tamarind liquid (see How To, page 212)	1/2 cup	125 mL
Fish sauce	1/4 cup	60 mL
Brown sugar, packed	2 tbsp.	30 mL
Cooking oil	1 tbsp.	15 mL
Tom yum paste	1 tbsp.	15 mL
Garlic cloves, minced	3	3
Chili paste (sambal oelek)	1 tsp.	5 mL
Sliced red onion	1 cup	250 mL
Chopped green onion (1 inch, 2.5 cm pieces)	3/4 cup	175 mL
Sliced green pepper	3/4 cup	175 mL
Sliced red pepper	3/4 cup	175 mL
Sliced yellow pepper	3/4 cup	175 mL
Cooking oil	1/4 cup	60 mL
Basa fillets, halved lengthwise	1 lb.	454 g
All-purpose flour	1/2 cup	125 mL

Stir first 3 ingredients and set aside.

Heat a wok or large frying pan on medium-high. Add cooking oil. Add next 3 ingredients and stir-fry for 30 seconds until fragrant.

Add next 5 ingredients and stir-fry for 3 minutes until vegetables start to soften. Stir in tamarind mixture and bring to a boil. Arrange on a serving plate.

Heat cooking oil in a large frying pan on medium-high. Dredge fillets in flour and cook for 2 minutes per side until golden and fish flakes easily when tested with a fork. Arrange over vegetable mixture. Serves 4.

1 serving: 383 Calories; 18.6 g Total Fat (7.0 g Mono, 3.6 g Poly, 3.0 g Sat); 51 mg Cholesterol; 38 g Carbohydrate; 3 g Fibre; 18 g Protein; 1554 mg Sodium

GARNISH
lime slices and wedges

ABOUT BASA
Although basa is often imported to North America from Vietnam, this fish is also native to the Chao Phraya basin in southern Thailand. It has a delicate texture and is widely available.

MAKE AHEAD
Cut vegetables and mix up sauces in individual containers up to one day in advance. Cover and refrigerate until ready to use.

Eclectic and enchanting, the resplendent colours and flavours in this dish will dazzle. Serve as a main entree accompanied by rice and simple stir-fried vegetables, or as one element of a multi-dish, Thai-themed dinner party.

Massaman Beef Curry

Cooking oil	1 tbsp.	15 mL
Boneless beef blade roast, cut into 1 inch (2.5 cm) pieces	1 1/2 lbs.	680 g
Chopped onion	1 cup	250 mL
Brown sugar, packed	2 tbsp.	30 mL
Thai red curry paste	4 tsp.	20 mL
Ground cumin	1/2 tsp.	2 mL
Ground cardamom	1/4 tsp.	1 mL
Ground nutmeg	1/4 tsp.	1 mL
Salt	1/4 tsp.	1 mL
Ground cloves	1/8 tsp.	0.5 mL
Turmeric	1/8 tsp.	0.5 mL
Prepared chicken broth	3/4 cup	175 mL
Can of coconut milk	14 oz.	398 mL
Chopped peeled waxy potatoes (1 1/2 inch, 3.8 cm, pieces)	4 cups	1 L
Finely chopped salted peanuts	1/4 cup	60 mL
Bay leaves	2	2
Cinnamon sticks (4 inches, 10 cm, each)	2	2
Fish sauce	1 tbsp.	15 mL
Tamarind liquid (see How To, page 212)	1 tbsp.	15 mL

Heat 2 tsp. (10 mL) cooking oil in a large frying pan on medium-high. Brown beef in 2 batches and transfer to a 3 1/2 to 4 quart (3 1/2 to 4 L) slow cooker.

Heat remaining cooking oil in pan. Add next 9 ingredients and cook for 5 minutes until onion is softened.

Add broth, stirring constantly until boiling. Stir in coconut milk.

Add next 4 ingredients to slow cooker and pour sauce over top. Cook, covered, on Low for 8 to 10 hours or on High for 4 to 5 hours. Discard bay leaves and cinnamon sticks.

Stir in fish sauce and tamarind. Makes about 6 cups (1.5 L).

1 cup (250 mL): 582 Calories; 39.6 g Total Fat (10.0 g Mono, 1.6 g Poly, 21.3 g Sat); 77 mg Cholesterol; 33 g Carbohydrate; 4 g Fibre; 25 g Protein; 737 mg Sodium

---

GARNISH
chopped roasted
 salted peanuts
cilantro leaves

ABOUT MASSAMAN CURRIES
Massaman curry is a spicy, coconut milk-based curry, usually made with beef, sometimes with chicken, and always with potatoes and peanuts. It is often served at special occasions such as weddings. It is thought to have originated in Muslim India, the word *massaman* being a variant of the word *muslim*. Although massaman curry paste is not easily found in North America, a substitute can be easily created by using common red curry paste and adding sweet spices to it.

MAKE AHEAD
As is the case with most curries, you can make and refrigerate this one up to two days ahead, and then reheat it. The flavours really benefit from a day or two of "steeping."

The slow cooker goes from mundane to exotic.
Consoling spices mingle and mellow,
and a subtle sweet heat
bathes the senses.

Grilled Chicken
in Pandanus Leaves

Oyster sauce	2 tbsp.	30 mL
Soy sauce	2 tbsp.	30 mL
Tom yum paste	2 tbsp.	30 mL
Brown sugar, packed	1 tbsp.	15 mL
Garlic cloves, minced	2	2
Sesame oil	1 tsp.	5 mL
Pepper	1/4 tsp.	1 mL
Boneless, skinless chicken thighs (about 3 oz., 85 g, each), halved	8	8
Pandanus leaves, cut into 5 x 1 inch (12.5 x 2.5 cm) pieces	32	32

Combine first 7 ingredients in a large resealable freezer bag. Add chicken and marinate in refrigerator for 6 hours or overnight. Drain and discard marinade.

Place 2 pandanus leaves, overlapping lengthwise, on work surface (see How To, page 215). Place 1 chicken piece in centre of leaves. Bring both ends up and secure with a wooden pick. Repeat steps. Cook on a greased grill on medium for 7 minutes per side until a meat thermometer reads 170°F (77°C). Makes 16 pieces.

1 piece: 77 Calories; 4.6 g Total Fat (1.2 g Mono, 0.7 g Poly, 1.2 g Sat); 28 mg Cholesterol; 1 g Carbohydrate; trace Fibre; 8 g Protein; 174 mg Sodium

ABOUT PANDANUS LEAVES
Popular in Thai and Malaysian cooking, these leaves can be added directly to your cooking, or they can be used to wrap dishes, enveloping them in a flowery aroma. Also known as *screwpine leaves*, pandanus leaves can be found in Asian markets.

MAKE AHEAD
Marinate the chicken up to one day in advance. Wrap marinated chicken in pandanus leaves up to three hours in advance. Cover and refrigerate until ready to cook.

GARNISH
pandanus leaves
strips of lime peel
small red chili peppers

Capture your guests' fancy; then, reward their interest.
Pandanus leaves add a woodsy vanilla-like note
to this dish, as well as a remarkable visual.
Fascinating presentation, superb flavour.

Coconut Sticky Rice
With Mango

Water	1 1/4 cups	300 mL
Long-grain glutinous rice, soaked overnight, rinsed and drained	1 cup	250 mL
Can of coconut milk	14 oz.	398 mL
Granulated sugar	3/4 cup	175 mL
Salt	1/4 tsp.	1 mL
Vanilla extract	1 tsp.	5 mL
Large mango, peeled and sliced	1	1
Sweetened medium coconut, toasted (see Tip, page 128)	2 tbsp.	30 mL

Bring water and rice to a boil in a large oven-safe saucepan. Reduce heat to medium-low and simmer, uncovered, for 9 minutes until liquid is evaporated and small craters have appeared. Cover and cook in a 300°F (150°C) oven for 15 minutes until rice is tender.

Bring next 3 ingredients to a boil in a medium saucepan, stirring constantly. Reduce heat to medium-low and simmer for 25 minutes until mixture is thick enough to coat back of a spoon. Remove from heat.

Stir in vanilla.

Transfer rice to a bowl. Gently stir in half of sauce and let stand for 5 minutes. Spoon rice mixture into 6 dessert dishes. Arrange mango slices over rice. Spoon remaining sauce over mango and sprinkle with coconut. Serves 6.

1 serving: 383 Calories; 15.0 g Total Fat (0.7 g Mono, 0.2 g Poly, 13.0 g Sat); 0 mg Cholesterol; 60 g Carbohydrate; 2 g Fibre; 4 g Protein; 110 mg Sodium

GARNISH
sprigs of mint

ABOUT LONG-GRAIN GLUTINOUS RICE
Despite its name, glutinous rice doesn't actually contain any gluten. However, it is sweeter than most varieties of rice. When cooked, glutinous rice becomes moist and sticky, making it easier to eat with chopsticks or form into shapes.

ABOUT MANGO
Mango trees are very common in Thailand, and resourceful Thais make the most of every part of the tree. Young leaves and shoots are eaten as accompaniments to a *nam prik* (nahm PRIHK) relish; unripe and semi-ripe mangoes are pickled, made into relishes or eaten raw with salt and chillies; and the ripe fruit is eaten on its own, alongside curries, as a sun-dried snack or made into a dessert paste.

Vietnamese cuisine is all about fresh, bright and spicy food, encouraging made-to-order flavour—such as with its satisfying soups. Ideal for casual, hands-on get-togethers, soups and spring rolls are served with garnishes of fresh herbs, lime, chili pepper and sauces, so guests can season their own bowls and rolls to taste. Get your hands on the freshest herbs and vegetables possible. Encircle your table with mismatched wooden chairs, recreating the earthy atmosphere of a traditional Vietnamese kitchen.

Vietnamese

Spicy Fresh

Mushroom Spring Rolls

Granulated sugar	1 cup	250 mL
Water	1/2 cup	125 mL
Lime juice	1/3 cup	75 mL
Fish sauce	1/4 cup	60 mL
Rice vinegar	2 tbsp.	30 mL
Chili paste (sambal oelek)	1 tsp.	5 mL
Chinese dried mushrooms, rehydrated (see Tip, page 84)	3	3
Dried cloud-ear mushrooms, rehydrated (see Tip, page 84)	2	2
Bean thread noodles, soaked in water for 15 minutes, drained	1 oz.	28 g
Large egg, fork-beaten	1	1
Uncooked shrimp (peeled and deveined), finely chopped	1/2 lb.	225 g
Lean ground pork	4 oz.	113 g
Finely grated carrot, squeezed dry	1/2 cup	125 mL
Finely chopped green onion	3 tbsp.	50 mL
Fish sauce	1 tbsp.	15 mL
Garlic clove, minced	1	1
Pepper	1/4 tsp.	1 mL
Rice paper rounds (6 inch, 15 cm, diameter)	22	22
Cooking oil	3 cups	750 mL

Stir sugar and water in a small bowl until sugar is dissolved. Stir in next 4 ingredients and set aside.

Thinly slice mushrooms and transfer to a bowl. Cut noodles into 2 inch (5 cm) lengths and add to mushrooms.

Add next 8 ingredients and mix well.

Place 1 rice paper round in a shallow bowl of hot water until just softened (see Tip, below). Place on a tea towel. Spoon about 2 tbsp. (30 mL) shrimp mixture along centre of rice paper round. Fold sides over filling and roll up from bottom to enclose. Transfer to a tray and cover with a damp tea towel. Repeat steps.

Heat cooking oil in a large frying pan on medium-high (see Tip, page 26). Shallow-fry spring rolls, 4 at a time, for 4 minutes, turning occasionally, until crisp and golden brown. Transfer to a paper towel-lined baking sheet to drain. Serve with dipping sauce. Makes 22 spring rolls.

1 spring roll with 1 tbsp. (15 mL) sauce: 84 Calories; 2.5 g Total Fat (1.2 g Mono, 0.5 g Poly, 0.5 g Sat); 29 mg Cholesterol; 12 g Carbohydrate; trace Fibre; 4 g Protein; 261 mg Sodium

GARNISH
butter lettuce leaves
sprigs of mint

MAKE AHEAD
Make and refrigerate spring rolls earlier in the day, and then reheat in a 375°F (190°C) oven for 15 minutes until heated through.

Eyes will light up at the sight. Crisp, light wrappers surround divinely flavourful filling, while a chili-speckled sauce invites dipping.

Kohlrabi Salad
With Lemon Grass Shrimp

Finely chopped green onion (white part only)	2 tbsp.	30 mL
Lemon grass paste	1 tbsp.	15 mL
Cooking oil	1 tsp.	5 mL
Dried crushed chilies	1/4 tsp.	1 mL
Salt, sprinkle		
Uncooked medium shrimp (peeled and deveined)	3/4 lb.	340 g
Cooking oil	2 tsp.	10 mL
Julienned kohlrabi	4 cups	1 L
Julienned carrot	1 cup	250 mL
Shredded fresh mint leaves, lightly packed	1/4 cup	60 mL
Lime juice	1/4 cup	60 mL
Fish sauce	2 tbsp.	30 mL
Garlic cloves, minced	2	2
Granulated sugar	2 tsp.	10 mL
Chili paste (sambal oelek)	1 tsp.	5 mL
Chopped salted peanuts	2 tbsp.	30 mL

Combine first 5 ingredients in a large resealable freezer bag. Add shrimp and marinate in the refrigerator for 30 minutes. Drain and discard marinade.

Heat cooking oil in a large frying pan on medium-high. Add shrimp and cook for 3 minutes until pink. Transfer to a bowl and set aside.

Combine next 3 ingredients in a large bowl.

Whisk next 5 ingredients and drizzle over kohlrabi mixture. Toss and transfer to a serving plate. Top with shrimp and sprinkle with peanuts. Makes about 8 cups (2 L).

1 cup (250 mL): 128 Calories; 4.3 g Total Fat (1.1 g Mono, 0.9 g Poly, 0.6 g Sat); 65 mg Cholesterol; 12 g Carbohydrate; 5 g Fibre; 12 g Protein; 564 mg Sodium

ABOUT KOHLRABI
Although kohlrabi is common in Asian cooking, it's actually native to northern Europe. This vegetable can be likened to cabbage in both taste and texture. When choosing kohlrabi, select bulbs that are under three inches (7.5 cm) in diameter and free of cracks.

MAKE AHEAD
Prepare all the vegetables, cook the shrimp and make the dressing, then refrigerate everything up to one day in advance. Toss all the ingredients with the dressing just before serving.

GARNISH
mint leaves

Crisp **kohlrabi** takes the spotlight where **green papaya** has traditionally appeared—but you won't miss it. Revel in the **fragrant** contrasts of shrimp, mint, peanuts and **chili heat**.

Pho Bo
(Beef Noodle Soup)

Medium rice stick noodles	1/2 lb.	225 g
Cooking oil	2 tsp.	10 mL
Thinly sliced onion	1 1/4 cups	300 mL
Water	4 cups	1 L
Prepared beef broth	4 cups	1 L
Cinnamon stick (4 inches, 10 cm)	1	1
Piece of ginger root (3 inch, 7.5 cm, length), halved	1	1
Star anise	2	2
Beef sirloin steak, thinly sliced (see Tip, page 208)	1 lb.	454 g
Fish sauce	2 tbsp.	30 mL
Granulated sugar	2 tbsp.	30 mL
Bean sprouts, trimmed	2 cups	500 mL
Thinly sliced red onion	1/2 cup	125 mL
Thinly sliced green onion	1/3 cup	75 mL

Cover noodles with hot water and let stand, covered, for 25 minutes until softened. Drain noodles and transfer to 6 serving bowls.

Heat cooking oil in a Dutch oven on medium-high. Add onion and cook for 5 minutes until browned.

Add water, stirring constantly and scraping any brown bits from bottom of pan for 1 minute. Add next 4 ingredients, reduce heat to medium-low and simmer for 15 minutes. Discard solids.

Stir in next 3 ingredients. Stir until beef is no longer pink.

Scatter remaining 3 ingredients over noodles, cover with beef and pour broth over top. Serves 6.

1 serving: *331 Calories; 7.9 g Total Fat (3.3 g Mono, 0.7 g Poly, 2.4 g Sat); 40 mg Cholesterol; 43 g Carbohydrate; 1 g Fibre; 22 g Protein; 1304 mg Sodium*

GARNISH
sprigs of cilantro
mint leaves
Thai basil leaves
small red chili peppers, thinly sliced
lime wedges

TIP
Set out a generous herb plate for your guests to personalize their pho. Use any of the garnishes listed.

ABOUT EATING PHO AUTHENTICALLY
Some believe there is a ritual one should follow when eating pho. Begin with a pair of chopsticks and a Chinese-style soup spoon. Before eating, add garnishes such as mint leaves, bean sprouts, cilantro and fresh chili peppers. You may also add squirts of lime juice and fish, hoisin or plum sauce to taste, although a well-balanced broth probably won't need alteration. Use the chopsticks to pile some rice noodles, a piece of meat, some herbs and sprouts and a little broth onto the spoon and then deliver the savoury delight to your mouth. Continue adding garnishes as desired until you've cleaned the bowl.

Offering an array of garnishes encourages guests to tailor the flavour. Fresh herbs by the handful, sprinkles of sliced chilies, shots of lime juice and sauces—every bowl unique.

Lemon Grass Curry Vegetables

Sesame oil	1 tbsp.	15 mL
Finely chopped shallots	3 tbsp.	50 mL
Curry powder	1 tbsp.	15 mL
Lemon grass, bulbs only, thinly sliced	3	3
Garlic cloves, minced	2	2
Granulated sugar	2 tsp.	10 mL
Sliced red pepper	1 cup	250 mL
Sliced yellow pepper	1 cup	250 mL
Frozen French-style green beans	2 cups	500 mL
Coconut milk	1 cup	250 mL
Fish sauce	1 tbsp.	15 mL
Salt	1/2 tsp.	2 mL

Heat a wok or large frying pan on medium-high and add sesame oil. Add next 5 ingredients and stir-fry for 1 minute.

Add red and yellow pepper and stir-fry for 1 minute. Add remaining 4 ingredients and cook for 3 minutes until vegetables are tender-crisp. Makes about 3 cups (750 mL).

1/2 cup (125 mL): 153 Calories; 10.7 g Total Fat (0.4 g Mono, 0.2 g Poly, 7.5 g Sat); 0 mg Cholesterol; 15 g Carbohydrate; 3 g Fibre; 2 g Protein; 428 mg Sodium

---

GARNISH
chopped fresh cilantro
sprigs of cilantro

ABOUT VIETNAMESE CURRIES
Often Vietnamese curries use a blend of spices similar to Madras curry powder, which contains a good dose of hot chilies as well as turmeric, coriander, cumin, cloves, cinnamon, bay leaves, fenugreek, allspice and black pepper.

A simple **stir-fry** with a shock of colour. Vibrant **peppers** and **beans** are coated in **sweet curry** sauce that is richly flavoured with **coconut** and **lemon grass** notes.

Ginger Garlic Gai-Lan

Gai-lan, trimmed and cut into 3 inch (7.5 cm) pieces (see Tip, below)	1 lb.	454 g
Cooking oil	1 tsp.	5 mL
Finely grated ginger root	1 tbsp.	15 mL
Garlic cloves, minced	2	2
Small red chili pepper, finely chopped (see Tip, page 148)	1	1
Water	1/4 cup	60 mL
Fish sauce	1 tbsp.	15 mL
Granulated sugar	1/2 tsp.	2 mL
Water	1 tsp.	5 mL
Cornstarch	1/2 tsp.	2 mL

Cook gai-lan in a large saucepan of boiling water for 1 minute. Drain well.

Heat a wok or large frying pan on medium-high and add cooking oil. Add next 3 ingredients and stir-fry for 1 minute until fragrant. Add gai-lan and stir-fry for 2 minutes.

Add remaining 3 ingredients and cook, covered, for 2 minutes until tender. Remove gai-lan to a plate with a slotted spoon.

Stir water and cornstarch until smooth. Add to wok and stir until bubbling and thickened. Remove from heat, add gai-lan and toss. Makes about 4 cups (1 L).

1/2 cup (125 mL): 35 Calories; 1.0 g Total Fat (0.3 g Mono, 0.2 g Poly, 0.1 g Sat); 0 mg Cholesterol; 6 g Carbohydrate; 1 g Fibre; 2 g Protein; 214 mg Sodium

ABOUT GAI-LAN
Also known as Chinese broccoli, this member of the cabbage family is a common vegetable in Asian cooking and often stands alone as a side dish. When choosing gai-lan, look for those with healthy leaves and firm, unblemished stalks.

TIP
Other vegetables you can use in this recipe are snow peas, bell peppers or asparagus. If you do substitute, omit the parboiling step and extend the wok cooking time slightly.

MAKE AHEAD
The gai-lan can be parboiled and refrigerated several hours in advance.

GARNISH
small red chili peppers

It won't take much to convince guests to eat these **greens**. Firmly textured **gai-lan** is tossed with a spicy **ginger garlic** blend for flavours familiar, yet **enticing**.

Stir-Fried Tofu
With Egg Noodles and Garlic Chives

Fish sauce	3 tbsp.	50 mL
Granulated sugar	3 tbsp	50 mL
Lime juice	3 tbsp.	50 mL
Tamarind liquid (see How To, page 212)	3 tbsp.	50 mL
Lemon grass paste	2 tbsp.	30 mL
Package of firm tofu, halved horizontally	13 oz.	370 g
Fresh, thin Chinese-style egg noodles	1/2 lb.	225 g
Cooking oil	2 tbsp.	30 mL
Chopped garlic chives (3 inch, 7.5 cm, pieces)	3 cups	750 mL
Thinly sliced red pepper	1 cup	250 mL

Stir first 5 ingredients until sugar is dissolved. Pour into a large resealable freezer bag and add tofu. Marinate in the refrigerator for 2 hours. Drain and reserve marinade. Set tofu aside.

Cook noodles in boiling water in a Dutch oven for 2 minutes, stirring occasionally, until tender but firm. Drain and cut in half.

Heat 1 tbsp. (15 mL) cooking oil in a large frying pan on medium-high. Cook tofu for 3 minutes per side until browned. Transfer to a cutting board and cover to keep warm.

Add remaining cooking oil, chives and red pepper to pan. Stir-fry for 2 minutes until softened. Add noodles and reserved marinade. Stir-fry for 3 minutes until heated through. Cook for an additional 2 minutes, without stirring, until bottom is almost dry. Transfer to a serving plate. Cut tofu into 1/8 inch (3 mm) strips. Arrange over noodles. Makes about 6 cups (1.5 L).

1 cup (250 mL): 305 Calories; 11.0 g Total Fat (2.7 g Mono, 1.9 g Poly, 1.5 g Sat); 39 mg Cholesterol; 41 g Carbohydrate; 3 g Fibre; 13 g Protein; 656 mg Sodium

---

GARNISH
blossom ends of garlic chives

ABOUT VIETNAMESE NOODLES
In Vietnam, noodles are more commonly available fresh than dried, and they are served as an ingredient in dishes, not on their own. Noodle dishes can be categorized as wet (soups), dry noodle bowls) or fried (stir-fries). Fried noodle dishes, be they stir- or pan-fried, are eaten as part of multiple-dish meals rather than on their own.

Delicate garlic chives, candle-like in appearance, rest atop marinated tofu and a tempting bed of noodles. Brightly tart tamarind is infused into this colourful stir-fry.

Caramel-Glazed Chicken

Fish sauce	2 tbsp.	30 mL
Garlic clove, minced	1	1
Lime juice	1 tsp.	5 mL
Dried crushed chilies	1/4 tsp.	1 mL
Boneless, skinless chicken thighs (3 oz., 85 g, each)	8	8
Granulated sugar	1/3 cup	75 mL
Water	3 tbsp.	50 mL
Boiling water	1/4 cup	60 mL
Finely chopped shallots	2 tbsp.	30 mL
Fish sauce	2 tbsp.	30 mL
Finely grated ginger root	1 tsp.	5 mL
Salt, sprinkle		
Pepper	1/2 tsp.	2 mL

Combine first 4 ingredients in a large resealable freezer bag. Add chicken and marinate in the refrigerator for 1 hour.

Heat and stir sugar and water in a small saucepan on medium until sugar is dissolved. Bring to a boil. Gently boil for 7 minutes, brushing sides of pan with wet pastry brush often, until medium brown.

Remove from heat and carefully add boiling water, stirring constantly. Add remaining 5 ingredients and return to heat, stirring until mixture is a syrup consistency. Transfer 2 tbsp. (30 mL) sauce to a small cup. Drain and discard marinade from chicken. Arrange chicken on a greased rack set in a baking sheet with sides. Broil on top rack in oven for 3 minutes per side until starting to brown. Brush with caramel sauce in small cup and cook for 3 minutes until chicken is no longer pink inside. Transfer to a serving plate and brush with remaining sauce. Makes 8 thighs.

1 thigh: 147 Calories; 5.7 g Total Fat (2.2 g Mono, 1.3 g Poly, 1.6 g Sat); 49 mg Cholesterol; 9 g Carbohydrate; trace Fibre; 14 g Protein; 741 mg Sodium

---

GARNISH
green leaf lettuce

ABOUT CARAMEL SAUCE
Caramel sauce is a key ingredient in Vietnamese cooking. Made mainly of white sugar that is heated until it's very dark brown, this sauce has an intensely savoury-sweet flavour and a rich, red-brown colour. Vietnamese caramel sauce is used to impart both rich flavour and colour, but only to savoury dishes, not to desserts.

Plated servings of **sweetly glazed** chicken, nestled with rice against **vibrant greens**, attract guests to their seats. Flavour layers of **shallot, garlic** and **chili** round things out deliciously.

Mushroom-Wrapped Halibut

Medium portobello mushrooms, gills and stems removed (see Why To, below)	4	4
Cooking oil	1 tbsp.	15 mL
Salt, sprinkle		
Pepper, sprinkle		
Tamarind liquid (see How To, page 212)	1 cup	250 mL
Brown sugar, packed	1/2 cup	125 mL
Fish sauce	2 tbsp.	30 mL
Soy sauce	2 tbsp.	30 mL
Lime juice	1 tsp.	5 mL
Halibut fillets (6 oz., 170 g, each), 1 inch (2.5 cm) thick, cut into eight 4 x 1 1/2 inch (10 x 3.8 cm) pieces	2	2

Brush mushrooms with cooking oil and sprinkle with salt and pepper. Broil on top rack in oven for 4 minutes per side until browned. Remove to a plate and cover with plastic wrap. Let stand for 15 minutes until softened. Cut into 1/4 inch (6 mm) slices.

Combine next 4 ingredients in a small saucepan and bring to a boil. Boil for 5 minutes, stirring occasionally, until mixture is syrupy.

Stir in lime juice. Reserve 1/3 cup (75 mL) sauce.

Brush half of remaining sauce over fish. Drape with mushroom slices. Brush with remaining sauce. Broil on centre rack in oven for 8 minutes until fish flakes easily when tested with a fork. Serve with reserved tamarind sauce. Makes 8 fillets.

1 fillet: 165 Calories; 2.8 g Total Fat (1.3 g Mono, 0.8 g Poly, 0.3 g Sat); 14 mg Cholesterol; 25 g Carbohydrate; 1 g Fibre; 11 g Protein; 710 mg Sodium

---

GARNISH
lime wedges

WHY TO
Because the gills can sometimes be bitter, be sure to remove them from the portobellos before broiling. First, remove the stems. Then, using a small spoon, scrape out and discard the mushroom gills.

Drink in the stimulating appearance of thick fillets draped with **portobello** slices. Heighten the dish with a **squeeze** of **lime** just before serving.

Spicy Tamarind Spareribs

Sweet-and-sour-cut pork ribs, trimmed of fat, cut into1-bone portions (see Tip, below)	3 lbs.	1.4 kg
Sliced lemon grass, bulbs only	1/2 cup	125 mL
Tamarind liquid (see How To, page 212)	1/2 cup	125 mL
Brown sugar, packed	1/4 cup	60 mL
Liquid honey	1/4 cup	60 mL
Soy sauce	1/4 cup	60 mL
Garlic cloves, chopped	4	4
Small red chili peppers, chopped (see Tip, page 148)	5	5

Put ribs into a large resealable freezer bag.

Process remaining 7 ingredients in a blender or food processor until smooth. Pour over ribs and marinate in the refrigerator for 2 hours. Arrange ribs in a single layer in a greased 9 x 13 inch (22 x 33 cm) baking dish and pour the marinade over top. Cover with foil and cook in a 350°F (175°C) oven for 1 hour until tender. Remove cover and skim any fat. Cook, uncovered (see Why To), for an additional hour, stirring every 10 minutes, until glazed. Serves 4.

1 serving: 803 Calories; 50.1 g Total Fat (21.6 g Mono, 4.7 g Poly, 18.9 g Sat); 165 mg Cholesterol; 49 g Carbohydrate; 1 g Fibre; 39 g Protein; 1490 mg Sodium

---

GARNISH
small red chili peppers
sliced lemon grass

TIP
The membrane or silverskin should be removed from the spare ribs before cooking. Baby back ribs can also be used in this recipe.

WHY TO
Baking with a cover on for the first hour will allow the spareribs to remain moist and to be very tender. Removing the cover for the last hour of baking will allow the marinade to thicken up and form a glaze.

Sharing never tasted so good. These spicy sweet morsels make for a delighted crowd—charming fingerbowls for every guest keep it clean.

Spicy Beef
With Roasted Lemon Grass Potatoes

Fish sauce	2 tbsp.	30 mL
Granulated sugar	2 tbsp.	30 mL
Soy sauce	2 tbsp.	30 mL
Garlic cloves, minced	3	3
Chili paste (sambal oelek)	2 tsp.	10 mL
Lemon grass paste	2 tsp.	10 mL
Pepper	1/2 tsp.	2 mL
Beef rib-eye steak, thinly sliced (see Tip, below)	1 lb.	454 g
Cooking oil	1 tsp.	5 mL
Baby potatoes, larger ones cut in half	2 lbs.	900 g
Butter	1/4 cup	60 mL
Lemon grass paste	1 tbsp.	15 mL
Salt	1/4 tsp.	1 mL
Pepper	1/8 tsp.	0.5 mL
Cooking oil	1 tsp.	5 mL
Coarsely chopped peanuts	2 tbsp.	30 mL
Thinly sliced green onion	3 tbsp.	50 mL
Small red chili pepper, thinly sliced (see Tip, page 148)	1	1

Combine first 7 ingredients in a large resealable freezer bag. Add beef and marinate in the refrigerator for 4 hours.

Heat cooking oil in a large frying pan on medium-high. Add potatoes and cook for 7 minutes, stirring occasionally, until browned.

Add next 4 ingredients and stir. Transfer to a 9 x 13 inch (22 x 32.5 cm) pan and bake in a 400°F (205°C) oven for 20 minutes, stirring once, until tender. Transfer to a serving plate.

Drain and discard marinade from beef. Heat a wok or large frying pan on medium-high. Add cooking oil. Add beef and stir-fry for 5 minutes. Spoon over potatoes and sprinkle with remaining 3 ingredients. Serves 4.

1 serving: 528 Calories; 22.7 g Total Fat (7.8 g Mono, 2.1 g Poly, 10.0 g Sat); 90 mg Cholesterol; 53 g Carbohydrate; 3 g Fibre; 27 g Protein; 1640 mg Sodium

---

GARNISH
romaine lettuce heart leaves
sliced English cucumber
cilantro leaves
sprigs of mint
lime wedges

TIP
Partially freezing the meat before slicing makes it easier to get attractive, evenly thin slices.

MAKE AHEAD
Assemble the vegetable garnish in advance and refrigerate until serving time. The potatoes require little effort and the beef cooks very quickly at the last minute, making this an excellent dish for entertaining.

Celebrate a higher level of taste. Beef slices
marinated in a **complex sauce**,
and **roasted** baby potatoes steeped
in **lemon grass** butter are cradled
beautifully by green **vegetables**
and herbs.

Strawberry and Papaya
With Lemon Grass Sabayon

Egg yolks (large)	4	4
Dry sherry	2 tbsp.	30 mL
Granulated sugar	2 tbsp.	30 mL
Lemon grass paste	4 tsp.	20 mL
Lemon juice	1 tsp.	5 mL
Sliced papaya	1 1/2 cups	375 mL
Sliced fresh strawberries	1 1/2 cups	375 mL

Whisk first 5 ingredients in a medium stainless steel bowl. Set over simmering water in a large saucepan so that bottom of bowl is not touching water (see How To, page 215). Whisk for 5 minutes until mixture is foamy and thickened enough to leave a path on the back of a spoon when you run your finger over it.

Arrange fruit on 6 serving plates. Drizzle with sabayon. Serves 6.

1 serving: 90 Calories; 3.5 g Total Fat (1.3 g Mono, 0.5 g Poly, 1.1 g Sat); 137 mg Cholesterol; 12 g Carbohydrate; 1 g Fibre; 2 g Protein; 78 mg Sodium

ABOUT PAPAYA
Although many are familiar with the tender, sweet flesh of fresh ripe papayas, the mild-tasting, crunchy flesh of unripened papayas is also a highly prized ingredient in the Vietnamese kitchen. It is pickled and used as a vegetable in soups and salads.

Vivid **fresh fruit** automatically attracts attention—but pour
a **sweet** and **creamy sabayon** infused with
lemon grass over top and the result will turn heads.

How-To Instructions

HOW TO FORM DUMPLINGS
(Page 14)

Spoon about 1 tbsp. (15 mL) filling onto centre of a wrapper. Moisten edges and gather up to form a cup shape.

HOW TO PREPARE DRUMMETTES
(Page 20)

Remove bony ends of drumettes with a sharp knife. Push meat up toward thick ends to expose bone.

HOW TO FORM SAMOSAS
(Page 44)

Divide pastry into 6 portions. Roll out each portion into a 6 inch (15 cm) circle and cut circles in half. Spoon filling onto each semicircle. Brush edges with egg. Fold over and seal.

HOW TO MAKE TAMARIND LIQUID
(Pages 46, 152, 156, 176, 180, 182, 200, 204 and 206)

Measure the amount of chopped tamarind pulp that corresponds to the desired yield (see chart, next page) and put into a small bowl. Pour the appropriate amount of boiling water over the pulp. Stir to break up pulp and let stand for 5 minutes. Press through a fine sieve and discard solids.

Measurements for Tamarind Liquid

Liquid yield	Pulp amount	Water amount
1 tbsp. (15 mL)	1 tbsp. (15 mL)	3 tbsp. (50 mL)
2 tbsp. (30 mL)	2 tbsp. (30 mL)	1/4 cup (60 mL)
3 tbsp. (50 mL)	2 tbsp. (30 mL)	1/3 cup (75 mL)
1/2 cup (125 mL)	1/4 cup (60 mL)	3/4 cup (175 mL)
3/4 cup (175 mL)	1/3 cup (75 mL)	1 cup (250 mL)
1 cup (250 mL)	1/2 cup (125 mL)	1 1/2 cups (375 mL)

HOW TO FORM MAKI
(Page 68)

Lay 1 nori sheet on work surface. Place 2 quarters, cut-side down, on bottom edge of nori sheet. Arrange next 3 ingredients along centre of rolls. Arrange remaining 2 rice roll quarters on top, cut-side up. Dampen top edge of nori sheet with a little water. Roll up tightly from bottom. Wrap with plastic wrap. Repeat steps. Chill for 1 hour and cut each roll into 8 slices.

HOW TO CUT DAIKON AND KABOCHA
(Page 78)

Use a small cookie cutter to cut through the peel of the kabocha pieces. Carefully trim the bordering peel away from the cut edges. With a paring knife, round the edges of the daikon pieces

HOW TO CUT GARNISHES
(Page 98)

Use small cookie cutters to cut the daikon into flowers, red pepper into leaf shapes, yellow pepper into circles and carrot into stars.

HOW TO ROLL GRAPE LEAF PACKAGES
(Page 120)

Spoon about 1 tbsp. (15 mL) lamb mixture onto vein side of each leaf. Fold in sides and roll to enclose filling.

HOW TO FORM FATAYER
(Page 124)

Roll out each dough portion on a lightly floured surface to a 4 inch (10 cm) round. Spoon about 1 1/2 tbsp. (25 mL) filling in centre of each round. Dampen edges of dough with water. Fold edges toward centre in 3 sections, forming a triangle. Press edges firmly to seal.

HOW TO ROLL BAKLAVA
(Page 136)

Cut layered pastry sheet crosswise into 3 rectangles. Spoon 1 1/2 tsp. (7 mL) filling along short edge of each rectangle. Fold long edges over filling and lay a drinking straw alongside filling. Roll up to enclose

and push both ends of roll toward centre to create a crinkled effect. Remove drinking straw.

Make 1 inch (2.5 cm) cuts halfway along each side of wrappers. Combine cooking and sesame oil and brush onto 1 side of wrappers. Press 12 wrappers, oil-side down, into 12 muffin cups. Press second wrapper, oil-side down, into each muffin cup, alternating points, to form a flower shape.

HOW TO FORM WRAPPER CUPS
(Page 140)

Place a large sheet of aluminum foil on work surface. Lay banana leaf, shiny side down, on foil. Arrange fillets in centre of leaf and spread lemon grass mixture over fillets. Bring up sides of leaf and fold over to enclose. Wrap tightly in foil.

HOW TO PREPARE BANANA LEAF PACKAGES
(Page 158)

HOW TO COOK SABAYON AND CHECK FOR THICKNESS
(Pages 160 and 210)

Set bowl of sabayon over simmering water in a large saucepan so that bottom of bowl is not touching water. Whisk for 5 minutes until mixture is foamy and thickened enough to leave a path on the back of a spoon when you run your finger over it.

HOW TO FORM SALAD ROLLS
(Page 164)

Arrange 3 basil leaves in centre of rice paper. Spoon about 1/4 cup (60 mL) vermicelli mixture over basil. Fold sides over filling and roll up from bottom to enclose.

HOW TO WRAP CHICKEN IN PANDANUS LEAVES
(Page 184)

Place 2 pandanus leaves, overlapping lengthwise, on work surface. Place 1 chicken piece in centre of leaves. Bring both ends up and secure with a wooden pick.

Glossary

Asian eggplant ~ see page 156.

Asian pear ~ see page 72.

banana leaves ~ see page 158.

basa ~ see page 180.

bean thread noodles ~ see page 170.

black bean sauce ~ this deeply flavoured seasoning is made from mashed fermented black beans that are seasoned with garlic and the light licorice flavour of star anise. Black bean sauce blends deliciously with many Asian dishes and is commonly used in Chinese, Korean and Vietnamese cooking.

black cardamom ~ native to India, this aromatic spice is a member of the ginger family. Unlike green cardamom's sweet flavour, black cardamom has a smoky aroma that mixes well in rich soups and stews. Although you can purchase cardamom already ground, it's best to use whole pods for a fuller flavour. For best results, crush the pods lightly with the back of a knife before using.

bulgur ~ see page 118.

cabbage kimchee ~ see page 92.

cardamom ~ see green cardamom and black cardamom.

char siu ~ see page 18.

chickpea flour ~ see page 42.

Chinese dried mushrooms ~ see page 28.

Chinese five-spice powder ~ this fragrant mixture gets its distinctive flavour from a combination of five different spices—usually cinnamon, cloves, fennel seed, star anise and Szechuan peppercorns.

Chinese rice wine ~ commonly referred to as *yellow wine*, this cooking and drinking wine is a staple of Chinese cuisine. Brewed from water and fermented rice, Chinese rice wine is mildly sweet and has a faintly nutty aroma.

Chinese-style egg noodles ~ see page 16.

coriander chutney ~ coriander and chutney are staples of Indian cuisine, and so is this combination of the two. Coriander chutney is made mainly from coriander seed, lime juice, chilies and salt. You may find the aroma familiar, as coriander is also called cilantro in its fresh form.

dashi granules ~ see page 84.

deep-fried tofu puffs ~ see page 70.

daikon radish/lo-bok ~ also known as *Japanese radish* or *Chinese turnip*, daikon is a large white root vegetable with a fresh, sweet flavour. When choosing daikon, look for those that are firm and smooth.

dried Indian black beans ~ see page 52.

edamame ~ see page 66.

enoki mushrooms ~ see page 104.

fish sauce ~ made from salted and fermented fish and available in many variations, this popular Southeast Asian condiment can be found at grocery stores or Asian markets. Fish sauce is used similarly to soy sauce and packs a strong, salty flavour that's essential to many Asian cuisines.

gai-lan ~ see page 198.

galangal ~ see page 152.

garam masala ~ a mixture of as many as 12 different spices, garam masala often includes black pepper, cardamom, cinnamon, cloves, coriander, cumin, dried chilies, fennel, mace and nutmeg. This blend is said to add warmth to both the spirit and the palate, which is fitting, since the Indian word *garam* literally means "warm."

garlic chives ~ this herb is similar to chives, but with an infusion of garlic flavour throughout the plant. Best when the flowers have yet to bloom, garlic chives can be used in both cooked and uncooked dishes. They can be stored, sealed, in the refrigerator for up to one week.

ghee ~ see page 40.

grape leaves ~ the large green leaves from grape vines make perfect wrappers for a variety of fillings. Popular in Greek and Middle Eastern dishes, grape leaves are rarely found fresh in North America, but canned and jarred varieties are available. Make sure to rinse them of the salty brine they are packed in.

green cardamom ~ this cranberry-sized pod is the sweeter version of its more savoury relative, black cardamom. Each pod contains about 15 to 20 seeds that provide a pleasant sweetness to a variety of South Asian dishes. To extract the full flavour from green cardamom, use fresh, whole pods. Feel free to leave the pods in your meal when serving to guests, as green cardamom is also used as a breath freshener.

jackfruit ~ see page 160.

Japanese seven-spice blend ~ also known as *shichimi togarashi*, this spice blend is commonly used in Japanese cooking and generally works well wherever pepper would normally be used. Japanese seven-spice is made of sansho chili peppers, seaweed, chili, poppy seeds, white sesame seeds, black sesame seeds and dried tangerine zest.

kabocha squash ~ see page 78.

kohlrabi ~ see page 192.

Korean hot pepper paste ~ a popular condiment in Korean cooking, this soy-based red pepper paste adds an appetizing heat to many popular dishes. Traditionally, the paste is made from scratch in large batches; however, the wide selection of prepared versions has made the traditional method of preparation less common.

Korean-style beef short ribs ~ see page 110.

Lebanese cucumbers ~ see page 122.

Lebanese seven-spice blend ~ also known as *baharat*, this spice blend is a popular seasoning for many traditional Lebanese dishes such as lamb kibbe. Do not confuse Lebanese seven-spice with Japanese seven-spice, as they have vastly contrasting flavours.

lemon grass ~ see page 174.

lemon grass paste ~ this smooth blend of lemon grass and other common Thai ingredients, such as coriander, chilies, peanut oil and ginger, is a delicious and convenient way to incorporate the fresh citrus flavour of lemon grass into your cooking. Lemon grass paste can be found in Asian markets and most grocery stores.

lime leaves ~ see page 154.

long beans ~ see page 24.

long-grain glutinous rice ~ see page 186.

lychee ~ native to Southeast Asia, this small red or brown fruit has a rough shell that covers a sweet and juicy white flesh. Choose those that are the brightest shade of red or brown and free of blemishes.

mirin ~ made from glutinous rice, this cooking liquid is essential in Japanese cuisine. One splash will bring a pleasant sweetness that complements many Asian dishes. Mirin is also referred to as *rice wine* and, once opened, it will keep in a refrigerator for up to three weeks.

miso ~ see page 74.

nori ~ these thin sheets of dried seaweed are a popular choice for wrapping sushi and other Asian finger foods. Nori has a sweet flavour and is rich in protein, vitamins and minerals. It can be purchased at Asian markets and some grocery stores.

okra ~ the long slender pods of the okra plant have become popular in dishes from America's South, but its origins are actually African. Suitable for broiling, baking, frying, pickling and stuffing, okra is adaptable to many recipes. When choosing fresh okra, look for young, unblemished pods that are slightly tender.

orange blossom water ~ this fragrant liquid is the product of distilled orange blossoms. The tart flavour blends well with many mixed drinks, baked goods and a variety of sweet and savoury dishes.

oyster sauce ~ this blend of oysters, brine and soy sauce is a popular ingredient in Asian cuisine, especially stir-fries. Oyster sauce is also used as a condiment, much like fish sauce and tamari.

pandanus leaves ~ see page 184.

paneer ~ also known as *panir*, this fresh, unripened cheese is common in Indian cooking. Paneer is made from whole cow or buffalo milk, curdled with either lemon or lime juice and the addition of whey. It is then pressed, which gives it a firm texture similar to that of tofu. Paneer is often served diced and sautéed in dishes such as dal and other lentil curries. It is also used as a protein in many varieties of vegetarian dishes.

panko crumbs ~ see page 168.

papaya ~ see page 210.

pomegranate molasses ~ see page 134.

pomelos ~ see page 172.

rogan josh sauce ~ see page 60.

round dumpling wrappers ~ see page 14.

saffron ~ see page 54.

sake ~ although sake is also known as *rice wine*, it is more accurately classified as a beer since it is produced from a fermented grain (rice) and not fruit. Good sake is generally dry tasting and can be used for both drinking and cooking. Once opened, it will keep in a refrigerator for up to three weeks.

sambal belacan ~ sambal is a condiment that is primarily composed of chilies, brown sugar and salt. Sambal belacan is a sambal that has a distinct infusion of toasted shrimp paste, making it a perfect partner for many Asian dishes.

short-grain rice ~ see page 94.

shrimp paste (belacan) ~ made from minced shrimp that is salted and fermented, shrimp paste adds a salty fish flavour to many Asian soups and sauces. Use shrimp paste sparingly, as its flavour has a concentrated pungency.

soba ~ see page 100.

sriracha chili sauce ~ an all-purpose hot sauce and dipping sauce, sriracha is a popular Asian condiment made mainly of hot chilies. Sriracha's flavourful punch goes well with an assortment of foods and is a tasty alternative to your usual hot sauce.

star anise ~ see page 20.

sumac ~ a maroon powder that is harvested from the dried berries of the sumac shrub. Sumac is tart tasting, with notes of lemon and pepper. It has widespread use in Middle Eastern cooking.

sweet chili sauce ~ this favourite Thai dipping sauce is made from chili peppers, vinegar, sugar and garlic. Store-bought sweet chili sauce has similar applications to sriracha chili sauce, but provides a subtler heat and sweeter flavour. However, traditional Thai recipes will vary the degree of heat from mild to extremely hot.

tahini ~ a thick paste made from ground sesame seeds. Tahini is a common ingredient in Middle Eastern cooking and is used to add flavour to such dishes as hummus and baba ghanoush.

tamari sauce ~ like soy sauce, tamari is made from soybeans; however, it is thicker and has a more mellow flavour. It is used directly in cooking and is also a popular condiment in Japanese kitchens.

tamarind ~ this fruit is desired most for its sour-sweet pulp, which is a key ingredient in Worcestershire sauce. Many Asian dishes benefit from tamarind's flavour. Tamarind is found in a variety of fresh and prepared forms at most Asian markets.

Thai basil ~ see page 164.

Thai red and green curry pastes ~ red or green Thai chili peppers and other flavourful ingredients are combined to make these fiery seasonings. Just a small amount will add an authentically Asian heat and flavour to your cooking—especially green curry paste, which is much hotter than the red variety.

tom yum paste ~ this paste resulted from the popularity of tom yum soup in Thailand. Tom yum paste is simply a prepared blend of tom yum soup's contrasting hot and sour flavours, including lemon grass, chili peppers, galangal, fish sauce and tamarind.

turmeric ~ this relative of the ginger plant is a key ingredient in the preparation of curry. Turmeric is intensely pungent and only a small amount is needed to enhance a dish's flavour and colour. It is also a primary ingredient in American mustard, providing a bright yellow colour.

wasabi paste ~ also known as Japanese horseradish, this green-coloured condiment has a sharp and spicy flavour. Sushi and sashimi are commonly served with a mixture of wasabi paste and soy sauce.

water chestnuts ~ see page 22.

za'atar spice blend ~ also spelled *satar* or *zahatar*, this herb blend is used extensively throughout the Middle East. Za'atar is commonly made of marjoram, oregano, thyme, toasted seeds, and salt.

Measurement Tables

Throughout this book measurements are given in Conventional and Metric measure. To compensate for differences between the two measurements due to rounding, a full metric measure is not always used. The cup used is the standard 8 fluid ounce. Temperature is given in degrees Fahrenheit and Celsius. Baking pan measurements are in inches and centimetres as well as quarts and litres. An exact metric conversion is given below as well as the working equivalent (Metric Standard Measure).

Spoons		
Conventional Measure	Metric Exact Conversion Millilitre (mL)	Metric Standard Measure Millilitre (mL)
1/8 teaspoon (tsp.)	0.6 mL	0.5 mL
1/4 teaspoon (tsp.)	1.2 mL	1 mL
1/2 teaspoon (tsp.)	2.4 mL	2 mL
1 teaspoon (tsp.)	4.7 mL	5 mL
2 teaspoons (tsp.)	9.4 mL	10 mL
1 tablespoon (tbsp.)	14.2 mL	15 mL

Cups		
Conventional Measure	Metric Exact Conversion Millilitre (mL)	Metric Standard Measure Millilitre (mL)
1/4 cup (4 tbsp.)	56.8 mL	60 mL
1/3 cup (5 1/3 tbsp.)	75.6 mL	75 mL
1/2 cup (8 tbsp.)	113.7 mL	125 mL
2/3 cup (10 2/3 tbsp.)	151.2 mL	150 mL
3/4 cup (12 tbsp.)	170.5 mL	175 mL
1 cup (16 tbsp.)	227.3 mL	250 mL
4 1/2 cups	1022.9 mL	1000 mL (1 L)

Dry Measurements		
Conventional Measure Ounces (oz.)	Metric Exact Conversion Grams (g)	Metric Standard Measure Grams (g)
1 oz.	28.3 g	28 g
2 oz.	56.7 g	57 g
3 oz.	85.0 g	85 g
4 oz.	113.4 g	125 g
5 oz.	141.7 g	140 g
6 oz.	170.1 g	170 g
7 oz.	198.4 g	200 g
8 oz.	226.8 g	250 g
16 oz.	453.6 g	500 g
32 oz.	907.2 g	1000 g (1 kg)

Oven Temperatures			
Fahrenheit (°F)	Celsius (°C)	Fahrenheit (°F)	Celsius (°C)
175°	80°	350°	175°
200°	95°	375°	190°
225°	110°	400°	205°
250°	120°	425°	220°
275°	140°	450°	230°
300°	150°	475°	240°
325°	160°	500°	260°

Pans	
Conventional - Inches	Metric - Centimetres
8 x 8 inch	20 x 20 cm
9 x 9 inch	22 x 22 cm
9 x 13 inch	22 x 33 cm
10 x 15 inch	25 x 38 cm
11 x 17 inch	28 x 43 cm
8 x 2 inch round	20 x 5 cm
9 x 2 inch round	22 x 5 cm
10 x 4 1/2 inch tube	25 x 11 cm
8 x 4 x 3 inch loaf	20 x 10 x 7.5 cm
9 x 5 x 3 inch loaf	22 x 12.5 x 7.5 cm

Casseroles			
Canada & Britain		United States	
Standard Size Casserole	Exact Metric Measure	Standard Size Casserole	Exact Metric Measure
1 qt. (5 cups)	1.13 L	1 qt. (4 cups)	900 mL
1 1/2 qts. (7 1/2 cups)	1.69 L	1 1/2 qts. (6 cups)	1.35 L
2 qts. (10 cups)	2.25 L	2 qts. (8 cups)	1.8 L
2 1/2 qts. (12 1/2 cups)	2.81 L	2 1/2 qts. (10 cups)	2.25 L
3 qts. (15 cups)	3.38 L	3 qts. (12 cups)	2.7 L
4 qts. (20 cups)	4.5 L	4 qts. (16 cups)	3.6 L
5 qts. (25 cups)	5.63 L	5 qts. (20 cups)	4.5 L

Tip Index

Recipe Index

Our website is filled with authentic cooking ideas

www.companyscoming.com

Save up to 75% on cookbooks
Discover free recipes and cooking tips
Sign up for our free newsletter with exclusive offers
Preview new titles
Find older titles no longer in stores

Company's Coming